William Shakespeare

Born: April 23, 1564

Died: April 23, 1616

Shakespeare's story is as romantic and dramatic as one of his own plays. He lived in a time of war, plague and desperate intrique, and soared to fame as Queen Elizabeth's favorite playwright. The author recounts the incidents and emotions which inspired his plays, and reveals the genius who even today continues to hold his place as the greatest poet and dramatist in all literature.

Books by Iris Noble

Biographies

CLARENCE DARROW
Defense Attorney

THE COURAGE OF DR. LISTER

THE DOCTOR WHO DARED
William Osler

EGYPT'S QUEEN
Cleopatra

EMPRESS OF ALL RUSSIA
Catherine the Great

FIRST WOMAN AMBULANCE SURGEON
Emily Barringer

GREAT LADY OF THE THEATRE
Sarah Bernhardt

JOSEPH PULITZER
Front Page Pioneer

LABOR'S ADVOCATE
Eugene V. Debs

NELLIE BLY
First Woman Reporter

NURSE AROUND THE WORLD
Alice Fitzgerald

PHYSICIAN TO THE CHILDREN
Dr. Béla Schick

WILLIAM SHAKESPEARE

Novels

COURAGE IN HER HANDS
MEGAN
ONE GOLDEN SUMMER
STRANGER NO MORE

William Shakespeare

by

IRIS NOBLE

JULIAN MESSNER

New York

Published simultaneously in the United States and Canada by
Julian Messner, a division of Simon & Schuster, Inc.,
1 West 39 Street, New York, N.Y. 10018. All rights reserved.

Sixth Printing, 1969

Printed in the United States of America

Library of Congress Catalog Card No. 61-7995

This book is respectfully dedicated to Mr. Macqueen-Pope, theatrical historian and descendant of that Thomas Pope who was fellow-actor with William Shakespeare, for the kindly, helpful suggestions he gave me one sunny afternoon in London.

William Shakespeare

1

It was five-thirty of a chill April morning and still dusk in the house when the boy came out of his second-story bedroom, yawned and stretched, then tiptoed down the stairs. In the kitchen the servant girl was hanging the iron kettle for porridge on its swinging hook inside the fireplace. She tousled his hair affectionately, and handed him the wooden basket of cold ashes. He smiled at her, staggering a little under the weight of the basket, and stepped outside.

It was cold. Will shivered and walked faster up Henley Street toward the pit-dump, pulling his leather jerkin closer around his chest. Why did he have to be the oldest boy in the family? Why couldn't Gilbert do this chore? But he never dared complain to his father. John Shakespeare was a good-natured man and easy on his children, but about this one chore he was adamant. Rain or snow, the ashes must be taken to the town dump.

Many years before Will was born, John Shakespeare and his friend Adrian Quiney had been fined for carelessly throwing rubbish into the street in front of their adjacent houses. Now, in 1577, Will's father, an alderman of the town of Stratford-on-Avon, felt it would be unseemly for him to be penalized for the same thing he had to fine others for doing.

So thirteen-year-old Will carried his burden to the dump heap every morning. This was his task, just as eleven-year-old Gilbert must be tumbling out of bed by now to put the table board up on its trestle forms and place the stools around it.

By the time he returned to Henley Street he was warm from

9

the exercise, the basket was empty and light. Will skipped on one leg from stone to stone. He threw a soft clump of earth at the Quineys' cat because it was stealthily climbing a tree to a birdnest. Then, suddenly, he forgot everything in watching the first rays of the sun break from behind a cloud and touch the town, picking the golden straw of a thatched roof, the soft rose of a brick chimney, the stone heights of Trinity Church.

Will had reached his house but, caught by the marvel of the sunrise, he could not go in. He watched, breathlessly, as the sun's rays slid down, spread out, to reach an old, twisted apple tree across the street. What had been, a second before, a cold, dark, somber mass of gnarled branches was now a golden thing of grace and beauty. The soft warmth of the sun moved slowly down the thick trunk to the ground and the shy, white flowers of the wild strawberries were like gleaming pearls in the rich, green carpet of their leaves.

Then came the sweet, high warbling of a skylark. Will Shakespeare took a deep breath. Why did such beauty, such song make him shiver with excitement? His brother Gilbert did not feel that way. The sun came up, the sun went down—why make a fuss about it?

"William," his mother called softly from the open doorway. "Come in, lad. You are late."

"Listen!" he commanded. The bird warbled again.

"Oh? The lark?" His mother smiled. "I like it, too; but what a strange boy you are to be thinking more of a bird's song than your porridge. Come, your father is waiting to say grace. He's impatient for breakfast."

A half-hour later he and Gilbert, with schoolbooks under their arms, were running down Henley Street. They slowed down, as other boys joined them, all dawdling and moving like snails. And no wonder—they had ten hours of school ahead of them. Nevertheless, promptly at six-thirty Will was in his seat. His friend Richard Field shared both bench and desk; today Richard was late and had to bend over for schoolmaster Thomas Jenkins' five cane strokes.

Richard eased his smarting self down onto the bench and whispered, "I have permission, Will. I may go with you and your father today."

Will smiled happily. It was his birthday today, April 23, and his Arden aunts had expressed a wish to see him, so his father was combining this birthday treat with business of his own to the northwest of Stratford.

The two boys bent over their *Caesar's Commentaries*. Will, who learned quickly and easily, rather liked Latin. At seven o'clock Master Jenkins gave the entire schoolroom a short lecture on the Bible. Then he heard the boys of Will's age recite their Latin while the younger students studied their *ABC's* from their hornbooks and the older ones read Greek.

At nine o'clock the boys were dismissed for recess, to eat the apples and oatcakes they had brought with them—and to play. In games of running and jumping or leapfrog, Will was as quick as any in the school, but he was too light for wrestling and the brawnier boys had him on his back in no time. Today two of the boys had brought long wooden swords and were enthusiastically but inexpertly dueling away in mock battle. When it was Will's turn to try he found that his quickness and agility in the parry-and-thrust gave him an advantage over the bigger boys.

The boys all returned to classes until eleven, when they were dismissed for lunch. School began again at one, with recess at three, then more lessons until six.

That day both Will and Richard had permission to leave school at midday to go with John Shakespeare to Wilmcote. Will's father had to buy leather for his glove shop and he also wanted to take a look at Asbies, a fine, big farm property that his wife had brought to their marriage, as her dowry.

They took a northwesterly road out of town, with John on one rented pony and the two boys on another. The ponies ambled and the boys talked.

"You have not been to Wilmcote before, Richard?"

"No, sir," he replied. "Did you not live on that Arden property, sir?"

11

"Aye," said John Shakespeare. "My father was naught but a tenant farmer of the Arden family, before whom we had to bow and scrape. But times are changing. If only my grandsire were alive to see me a man of business in Stratford and married to an Arden daughter! Not one hundred years ago—not fifty—a man lived and died in his station of life and could never get out of it. Everyone had his place—the lord, his knights, his soldiers, his farmers who tilled his soil and gave him the best of the produce. Not," he added hastily, "that the Shakespeares were not of good stock. Somewhere there's an ancestor who fought at Hastings and was promised a coat of arms for it."

"If you had it would you be a gentleman, Master Shakespeare?" asked Richard.

"I would, lad. I've made application for it. If it comes, I can sign myself 'John Shakespeare, Armiger.' Then I'll be a gentleman." He grinned broadly, his cheeks reddening with pleasure at the thought.

The name "gentleman" had a special place in law and society, and was not used carelessly. Only those who could boast a coat of arms could truly claim it.

"It's a changing world." Will's father returned to his theme. "And who knows what you two lads may rise to become? Richard, you go to London when you are sixteen to be apprenticed to a stationer. You may become Lord Mayor. As for Will, I don't know. He has the wits and brains but not the taste for trade, and it's the tradesmen and merchants who are getting the taste and power of money these days."

"My father says there are many merchants in the City Corporation in London, so powerful they even quarrel with the nobles at times."

"And a good thing too. The lords and princes had it all their way in England and what did they bring us?" declared merchant Shakespeare. "Wars and pillage and famine and it's time the peaceful men of business had their way. Under our good Queen Elizabeth there'll be no Dukes of York or Lancaster with their War of the Roses. What did they do for Englishmen but overrun their crops with their armies and burn their homes if they happened to speak for the wrong side? If my grandfather had spoken out as I just have he would have been whipped for it."

John Shakespeare straightened proudly in his saddle. There were coins in his pockets, he owned land, his son was learning Latin. He had taken a long step away from the serfdom under which his ancestors had lived.

"Look!" Will spoke for the first time. "Look!" He pointed to three dappled deer, their brown coats shining in the sun that filtered through the trees.

"So that's why you've been so silent, Will?" His father shook his head. "Never saw a boy so noticing of everything—berry bush or rabbit run or deer trail or fish pool. Do you expect to be hunter or woodsman when you grow up?"

"No, Father." He blushed and John Shakespeare laughed. But the blush was not what the older man thought. Will would have loved to be forester or woodsman or hunter except for one thing. He was sickened at the sight of slain woodland creatures —deer, rabbit or bird—who seemed to love life as much as he did. This was his secret and he was ashamed of it.

All three rode in peaceful silence for the next hour. There was much to see of great, spreading greenwood trees and sunny small clearings where violets and buttercups grew. Will scarcely knew the others were with him. From the moment they had left Stratford he had been in a fever of delight for the holiday and his eyes had been everywhere, over checkerboards of yellow and green fields and orchards. But the best of all was this mysterious, enchanted Forest of Arden. All too soon they left the wood and came to Wilmcote.

It was the first glimpse Richard Field had of the grand manor of the Ardens. Neither castle nor mansion, Wilmcote was a gentleman's home. The Ardens were a distinguished family in Warwick and the older son had inherited the great home estates. This smaller estate of Wilmcote had fallen to the younger son, Robert, the father of eight girls of whom Mary Arden Shakespeare was the youngest.

13

John Shakespeare's rap on the door brought a maid who conducted them into the great hall. It was hung with real tapestries, not painted cloths such as were all the Shakespeares and Fields could afford. Here were fine chairs with tall, curved backs and great chests for the linen and pewter. It was a big room, making the two figures in it look small as they bent over their looms.

But if the two ladies were small, they were also straight-backed and arrogant, with none of Mary's charm and warmth and prettiness.

"Good day, John," the older woman said. "How is our sister? And this is the boy? We have not seen him for a year. He has grown tall and has the slender look of the Ardens about him and nothing of you."

"Well, boy, have you forgotten your manners?" said the other, putting aside her work and looking at him sharply. "Did not your mother teach you how to greet a lady?"

Flushing with embarrassment, Will took off his cap, extended his foot and made a low bow, bringing arm and cap in a wide sweep across his body. Richard bobbed his head, thankful that he did not have to attempt a bow.

After John Shakespeare left to attend to his business the aunts thawed a little and seemed kinder. "Sit down on these footstools, lads. Now tell us, Will, how is thy conduct? Are thee respectful to thy parents? Seemly in thy manners? Industrious in thy studies?"

While he blundered through his answers Will wished with all his heart he could be Richard and just sit there saying nothing. But the ladies, quickly satisfied, smiled fondly at him and one of them clapped her hands. As a servant entered with plates of wild strawberries and cream, the boys were shown to a table where, all their restraint and embarrassment forgotten, they were free to stuff themselves full of strawberries, sugar meats, gingerbread and a wonderful cake called marchpane, made of pounded almonds, sugar and flour.

"We haven't forgotten it is your birthday, Will," the older aunt said. "We have a fine cap for you of plum-colored velvet, but you must have your mother crop your hair more neatly. The best gift you may not take home with you now; we will keep it for you until you are sixteen."

She took from the wall the long, silver-handled sword that had been his grandfather's. Will was allowed to touch it, even make a few lunges with it, before it was put back.

"It becomes you, lad. You have good bearing for so young a boy. Now we are to have entertainment. The carpenter begged permission to gather two of the plowmen, the weaver and several of the house servants to perform the morality play they did last Twelfth Night for us. It is only an excuse to get out of work, but we thought you would enjoy it and there is no harm in such tales of moral virtue."

Greatly excited, the boys watched the preparation being made for the play. Servants were quickly moving the long dining tables out of the way to make more space. Suddenly a man entered from a side door, paused abruptly at sight of the two boys and made as if to turn and go out. Then he stopped, for the boys had recognized him.

"It is our old schoolmaster, Simon Hunt," Richard said in surprise.

"Master Hunt." Will stood up and bowed. "We had not thought to see you here." He fell silent as he noticed a look of alarm in the oldest aunt's eyes.

"It is a while since I taught you Latin in Stratford, William and Richard. Have you improved?" The man was tall, his face thin. He turned to the older Arden woman, whose hands were clenched tightly in front of her. "I just happen to be passing and my horse was lame so I stopped——"

"Of course." She tried to sound calm but her voice was frightened.

"I am glad you came—you can tell us of William's education."

Simon Hunt put his hands on the boys' shoulders. "They are rascals, but there is as much good in them as mischief. What shall I say of you, Will? You have a good mind and good memory and could be the best student in all Stratford—if you were not also a dreamer. A lively tongue but never a mean, disloyal,

15

gossiping one." With those words the schoolmaster's hand tightened on Will's shoulder, as if in warning.

The boy suddenly understood: Simon Hunt and his aunts were in danger. He remembered certain whispered conversations between his mother and father and realized what they meant. He looked up at his former teacher and tried to say with his eyes that he could be trusted and there was no danger from him. But, he wondered, what about Richard?

Luckily at that moment there was an interruption. The carpenter stuck his head around the door from the kitchen and asked if they could begin now. Simon Hunt left the room with the older aunt and the other one bustled herself and the two boys onto a bench where they could see everything clearly. The play began.

A grotesque figure, giggling and choking under the red mask of the Devil's face, stepped out from behind the kitchen screen and announced, "For your pleasure, gentle lady and young masters, we present a story of the struggle of Good and Evil for the soul of man."

He retreated. A character representing Man entered, followed by the costumed figures of Greed, Laziness, Gluttony and Lust. These creatures of sin pleaded, coaxed and did their best to entice the Man to fall into their wicked ways, and for a while he listened to them. But soon out came Goodness and all the virtues.

The struggles, the arguments, the waverings of Man were an old story to Will and Richard, who had seen many morality plays before. It was made more exciting for Will because this was being given just for him, in honor of his birthday. Both boys knew that the great and noble families hired players to come to their mansions and entertain them, but the only plays that either of them had ever seen had been in the market place or in the Guild Hall.

Of course, these actors were amateurs, but that only made it the funnier. Will and Richard laughed hard at their mistakes, especially when Gluttony forgot his lines and everything stopped while the others whispered to him. And how tense it was when the Devil appeared to claim Man and Goodness finally banished Evil. It did not matter to the boys that the Man got angry at the way the Devil pulled at him and said in his natural, everyday voice, "There's no need to rip my clothes off, Dicon!" It could not spoil their enjoyment.

Then it was over. Will noticed that his aunt had come back but Master Hunt was not with her. The boys thanked the aunts and left.

2

They mounted the pony which had been loaded with saddle-bags of farm produce for the Shakespeares. Now, with the bumpy bags, the carefully wrapped parcel containing the velvet hat in front of Will, it was an uncomfortable ride for both boys who were tired from all the excitement. For several miles neither spoke. Then Richard burst out: "Master Hunt! 'Tis said he is a secret Jesuit and left Stratford rather than be forced out of the school. I do not believe he just rode up. Your aunts are protecting him. Are they Catholics too?"

"It is not our affair," Will answered shortly. "Keep a quiet tongue in your head, Richard, and say nothing about this to anyone."

"I will tell whom I please." Cabbages were banging against Richard's legs and the hurt made him angry at everyone. "Your aunts are wicked—they'll be imprisoned for sheltering a Jesuit."

Will pulled the horse to a halt and shifted in his seat so that he could look straight into his friend's face. "What does it matter? Papist or Puritan or English Church? I don't care. There be thieves and rogues in all and good men in all. My father is staunch English Church but when he and the Town Council had to order all the old Papist paintings in the Guild Chapel to be smeared over, he said it hurt him to do it because they were beautiful. Why should men hate each other for religion?"

Richard was aghast. "I never heard one talk so, Will Shakespeare!"

18

"I don't care about that. Just don't go bearing tales about my aunts."

"You call me a tale bearer?" Richard's pride was injured. "I'll give you a clout for that!"

Suddenly both boys had tumbled to the ground, grappling and punching each other, kicking and squirming. Richard, the stronger and the most angry, was managing to pin Will down, when they heard a noise that stopped the fight instantly.

"Quick! Get the pony off the road and behind those bushes. They may be robbers."

Before they could do more than move halfway off the wide lane, the troupe of riders was upon them and a voice called out gaily:

"This is the way to Stratford?"

"Yes, sir," Will answered. "Straight on a few miles."

The riders pulled to a halt. The boys stared, open-mouthed, at eight men on tall, sturdy horses, all dressed in fine tawny or dark brown leather riding breeches and doublets of olive green, curving in at the waist and sharply flaring over the hips. On their heads they wore velvet caps with great white plumes. Short capes swirled at their shoulders. But what was most dramatic was the sight of a small boy, about Will's age, who was dressed exactly like the others even to the feathers.

Behind them was a small cart, drawn by a tired and steaming horse and driven by a man in plainer clothes.

"And just how far is a 'few' miles?" The speaker was a tall man of middle age, his hair trimmed level with his shoulders and just beginning to turn gray. Deep furrows lined his mouth and there were heavy wrinkles about his eyes.

"Not more than three, sir."

"Then we dismount here to pound some of the dust from ourselves and put on our tabards." He climbed down, the others followed. He asked the boys, "Is there water nearby? We are both thirsty and dirty."

"We'll get it for you," Richard said eagerly. He and Will ran off into the woods, quickly located a pool of water from a running spring, filled the half-dozen gourds the tall stranger had given them, and hurried back to the road.

"Are you soldiers?" Will asked as he handed the tall man a gourd. The men had stripped off their doublets and were putting on close-fitting silken jackets of dark blue trimmed with yellow, all of which bore the same coat of arms on the sleeves.

"Nay. We are players under the patronage of the Earl of Leicester and we wear his livery."

Players! Will and Richard looked at each other. What a strange day this had turned out to be. First a morality play at the Ardens' and now these men! Of course these were real, professional actors. The boys knew they should hurry home, but nothing could drag them away just yet.

One of the players strolled up to the tall man, who was splashing water over his hands and face. "We may not be soldiers, but no one can say we do not have our battles, James Burbage. We're caught between the fire of the Puritans of the City and the fire of the Queen. It was bad enough when we visited London now and then to perform in one of the inns, but you have stirred the Puritans to fury with the building of your Theatre. It's too new and strange a thing, Burbage. They'll not accept it."

The man called Burbage was unruffled. Drying his hands with his handkerchief, he said, "My building stands outside the city limits. Words from the City Corporation cannot hurt me if the Queen, bless her, stands firm. We'll show her some pretty plays and interludes this Christmas and she'll let the Theatre stand."

Out of the corner of his eye Will had been watching the young boy with the players. He was copying the actions of the older men, walking about with the same swagger, tossing his small cape with the same swashbuckling grace. Now he walked over to the Stratford boys.

"Do you live nearby, lads?" he asked condescendingly.

Will scowled, furious at both the tone and the words. "We live in Stratford—where they teach better manners than you have learned. My father is alderman there."

The tall man was startled, then he put back his head and

laughed. "Richard," he said to the red-faced boy, "you deserved that. Ask pardon, my son, for trying to act the lord." He turned to Will. "If your father is alderman, is the name Shakespeare?"

"It is, sir."

"Then we shall have no trouble. He granted us the license to play in the town when we were here a couple of years ago. But I have forgotten—what are the accommodations in Stratford? The Inn at Coventry had fine beef but poor sherry; the inn at Oxford was the best but we had a crowd of discourteous students from the university who watched us and interrupted our performance with their own wit. They clapped for the clowns and the acrobats but they called our interludes poor things compared to their own performances of Latin plays by Terence and Plautus."

An actor came up to Burbage, his hands busy tightening the ruff around his neck. "Maybe," he said, "those students understand the gabble of Latin and can sit for three hours watching the mincing and posing they call acting, but you must be mad to be thinking of doing the same. Even in English such a play would run for two hours. *Two hours*, James! An interlude of ten, fifteen, twenty minutes is all right—that's the way we've always done it—but it's a mistake to stretch out a story any longer. It's the clowns and the jigging for such as Stratford and a pageant for the Queen that's wanted."

Richard tugged at Will's sleeve and whispered that it was late and they should be riding home, but Will was too fascinated to leave.

He knew what an interlude was. Between the buffoonery of the clowns and the dancing jigs and the singing of ballads were short interludes in which stories were acted out. Sometimes they were comic tales; sometimes they were morality plays like the one they had seen at the Arden home. Sometimes they were frivolous, with goddesses like Venus and Fortune debating who ruled the hearts of men.

"What do they mean by a *play*?" he asked the boy. An apolo-

21

getic smile from Richard; an answering grin from Will and the two had wiped out their first dislike of each other.

"Well, the students at the university have started acting out long stories, broken up into acts and scenes, and my father wants to try something like it tomorrow. If it is successful it would be a fine novelty for London," Richard Burbage replied.

"I see. What's the Theatre they're talking about?"

The boy's face was full of pride. "That's a building my father put up last year for shows. There's never been anything like it before. We play there and so do other acting companies, and they pay us instead of paying an innkeeper for the use of his courtyard. When we go back there'll be shows at the Theatre nearly every day in the week."

Will was dumbfounded. "But don't the folk in London work? Can they take a holiday every afternoon?"

"Oh, you don't know how many people there are in London. Why, five hundred people a day can see our shows and there's still thousands left to run the shops and do the work of the City."

Will had difficulty accepting this idea. But his attention was diverted when another actor came over, sat down on a rock and bent his head so that young Richard Burbage could fasten the ruff around his neck. "I'm with James Burbage on this. Let's try the play. It'll be in good, plain English. Robert Wilson here wrote it and there's no better place to try it out than Stratford. If it doesn't succeed—well, I'd rather be laughed at here than in London. If it does succeed, we can rehearse that play by Nicholas Udall, for London."

"And I say they'll chase us out of Stratford," another player spoke up passionately. "The crowds want what we've been giving them. Besides, how else can people know what's going on in the world if we don't tell them? We sing them songs about the Queen and the trouble with King Philip of Spain, songs about the weavers and the Flemish trade, songs about Drake and his expeditions or Raleigh and his foolish dreams of a colony in the New World. That's what people want—not a long, tedious tale."

The one called Wilson came up to him. "Would it be that

you are not anxious for our Theatre to succeed, John, now that your brother Henry is building the Curtain Theatre to compete with ours?"

John Laneham leaped to the ground, his sword flashing in his hand, but swift as he was, James Burbage was swifter and put himself between the two men.

"Nay, an end to this! I'll have no swordplay or brawling in my company."

Richard tugged at Will's sleeve. "Let us be going. It's late."

Reluctantly Will mounted the pony and Richard Field scrambled on behind him. They would have said good-by but the men were still in a heated argument and only the actor boy saw them leave and waved farewell.

They made the pony go at a fast trot, but just before they reached town Will slowed down so he could speak:

"I'm sorry if I have made us late and your father is angry."

"I doubt he will be, but he would if he knew we had been talking to those men. He says they are rogues and vagabonds who set a bad example to honest working people. He says it is all a trick, having the patronage of some lord, so they can evade the law which imprisons masterless men. So you will say nothing about it, Will?"

"If you will say nothing about Master Hunt and my aunts."

"Agreed." Then Richard added, "I wouldn't have anyway. I'm no tale bearer. But you made me angry."

So they rode sedately into town, left the pony at the stable and then separated to hurry to their homes.

Will's mother was watching for him, anxiously, at the door and the sight of him safe and sound and the gifts he handed her from her sisters made her forget to scold him. Only when he told her of the meeting with Master Simon Hunt did her face lose its lovely smile and become tense.

"He is only resting there a day or two, I am sure, before he makes for France and safety. What of Richard? Will he speak of what he saw?"

"No, Mother. I have his promise."

Nothing had ever been said to him directly, but from over-hearing whispered conversations between his father and mother he knew that this question of religion was a problem for them, just as it was for many families and friends. The Church of England had broken away from the Catholic Church during the reign of Queen Elizabeth's father, Henry VIII, and now Catholics were liable to prosecution if they were too open about their beliefs, went to Mass or sheltered priests. Even the Queen's cousin, Catholic Mary of Scotland, was a prisoner in Sheffield Castle. Matthew Parker, Archbishop of Canterbury, was a wise and tolerant man; as long as he had his say, Catholic and Protestant could live side by side in England, but local sheriffs and Protestant bishops sometimes interpreted the law more harshly.

Mary Arden had been born and raised a Catholic; her family was still openly Catholic. As wife to Alderman Shakespeare, she went to his church, keeping her own loyalties hidden, and the couple had achieved a mutual respect and tolerance for each other's viewpoints that was rare. Will had learned the same tolerance from them.

That evening as the family sat before the fire he told them about the players.

"May we go tomorrow to see them, please?" Gilbert begged, envious of the splendid day Will had had.

"Not if it is in the afternoon. Will may not leave school another day and you, Gilbert, are behind in your studies."

Then, while his mother spun wool and Gilbert and six-year-old Joan played tick-tack-toe, and his father went over his accounts, Will dreamed to himself in his corner. He had traded places with young Burbage. Dressed in a fine silk doublet and wearing a short cape and a hat with plumes, he was traveling far, far away from Stratford, down into the southern counties, seeing all the strange sights and people. He was going to London where the Queen lived . . .

A sudden sound brought him back to reality. It was the sound of rain against the windowpanes. He smiled joyfully to himself. If the rain continued the next day, he would see the play.

3

The young Shakespeares got their wish. The players could not appear in the open courtyard inn the following afternoon, and asked permission to use the Guild Hall that evening instead. Will and Gilbert sat with their parents in the very front row, where they could easily see everything.

There were clowns and acrobats, ballads, jigs and morris dances, but Will was impatient for the play that the actors had been talking about.

It was different from anything he had ever seen before. The story was about a prince who had been enchanted and turned into a dragon by a wicked brother. What made it so different was that just when Will thought it was all over, another act began.

After so much excitement school seemed burdensome and the next day Will had a hard time putting the actors out of his head. But as the days and months went on, he almost forgot them. He might complain to his brother and his friend Richard about the easy life that actor boy had, about the long hours of school and the schoolmaster's cane, but Will loved learning. Not only was his mind exceptionally quick; it was intense. He flung himself into any subject that interested him with passionate absorption, and he especially enjoyed history and anything that concerned people.

Life in Stratford for a young boy was full of dreary routine, but it also had plenty of diversion. There were the May Days and other festivals, there was the crowded marketplace once a week. There were hours fishing on the banks of the river Avon and playing games in fields and forests. Sometimes Will helped his father in the glove shop that was a part of their home, but he escaped that task whenever he could.

News from London and the rest of England flowed into Stratford by way of peddlers and tinkers. The players, of course, were best able to put into words what the ordinary man could not quite express about the events taking place in the world. Sometimes merchants from London came to buy wool, and often stayed the night with Alderman Shakespeare in Henley Street, instead of at the inn. On these occasions Will crouched on his stool listening to his elders talk of Sir Walter Raleigh and of Sir Francis Drake and of Queen Elizabeth.

Three years flew by, and at sixteen such news came to have much more meaning for Will. England was bursting its old seams with new vitality. For centuries there had been warfare between English nobles but Henry VIII had gathered a great deal of power into his own hands and passed it on to his daughter Elizabeth.

The country was expanding in many ways—in commerce, in trade, in explorations, on the high seas. Fifty years before, a village in England might not know what was going on a hundred miles away, while now Stratford folk talked about King Philip of Spain, about the court of London, and even about the New World across the great ocean, which was being explored.

Never had England such a ruler as Good Queen Bess. She was stubborn, willful, imperious, compromising; she seemed to change favorite advisers as often as she changed her gowns. But she was the Queen and the people adored her because she liked the same things they did. She wanted peace; so did they. She spoke several languages but she also used good down-to-earth English. She loved to be entertained, and when she traveled throughout the country she made the nobles pay for putting her and her great entourage up for the night and for showing her extravagant amusements—she enjoyed the joke on them and so did her people.

Only the noblemen chafed at peace. War would bring them glory, give them back their rightful place as chivalric defenders of England. Without it, they were useless, unnecessary. The few who saw the warning signs and realized that England's future wealth would flow more from trade and commerce than from farmland and sheep, invested money in merchant ships. But most of them sat on the riches they still received from their great estates and brooded. Who were these upstarts Hawkins and Drake and Raleigh, who fought Spain on the high seas almost as if they were pirates, burning Spanish ships and stealing the gold, instead of leading mailed and helmeted armies into battle?

England's arch-enemy was Philip of Spain, to whom Elizabeth lied, gave her word and broke it, always temporizing, always keeping him off-balance.

As all this news filtered into Stratford in scraps, youths grew restless for London or the sea. Will also felt it, especially when Richard Field, at sixteen, left for London to be apprenticed to Master Vautrollier, the printer and stationer.

But, just as quickly as a man could rise in those times, so could he fall. John Shakespeare had risen swiftly, steadily in the world; now his affairs snowballed downhill. He had invested in too many ventures. He had attempted to be a glover, operate the large property of Asbies, was part owner of a smaller property with his brother Henry, bought and sold wool, leather and other goods on a large scale. In addition, his duties as Chief Alderman took up a lot of his time.

When he was prosperous he had been glad to lend money. Or if a friend like Richard Hathaway or his brother Henry needed money, John would go as surety on the bond. Trouble seemed to strike them at the same time. They could not pay their loans, their creditors turned to him to make the money good. He himself was hard pressed for there had been a drop in the price of wool, a poor crop at Asbies, and other misfortunes. He had to borrow more money, make more economies. So when Will was sixteen and just finished with Stratford Grammar School he was told the bad news.

"I cannot send you to the university, son, not even if you receive one of Sir Hugh Clopton's scholarships." His father's round cheeks seemed to sag with age and unhappiness. "You will have to stay home and help me in the shop."

That year, late in 1579, his little sister Anne sickened and died. Now Will was glad he had not complained. Mary Shakespeare's grief, and the way she laid aside her own sorrow to comfort him and the others, was something he never forgot.

But he was still only sixteen, not yet a man. He hated having to sit for long hours in the glove shop, bent over the leather with the glover's paring knife, cutting and fashioning all the different kinds of gloves, mitts and gauntlets. His back ached, his legs grew stiff, every muscle longed to be free and out of there. John Shakespeare knew this, and he gave Will a holiday as often as he could.

"You are too soft with him," his neighbor the blacksmith said.

"Perhaps but he is young. I feel ashamed I could not send him to Oxford. The stories that boy tells us in the evenings, from his Greek lessons! So if he wants to wander the forest and dream a little, it isn't much he asks."

On his holidays Will enjoyed roaming the forest without purpose, sometimes running through a meadow with a wild burst of energy, sometimes listlessly following deer tracks into the depths of the Forest of Arden where few other people ever went. Sometimes he would climb up onto the low branches of a great oak and pretend he was Robin Hood with a band of merry outlaws. Or he would sit by a shadowy pool and remember the plays he had read in school and imagine he saw around him Greek gods and goddesses, nymphs, shepherds and shepherdesses.

Other times he would desert the forest and follow country lanes that led to Kenilworth, the castle of the Earl of Leicester. Sitting on a flat rock, his slender arms wrapped around his knees, Will would gaze at the looming towers and stone battlements, and dream a whole pageant of knights, queens in distress, kings with crowns on their heads. He would pretend to be the Earl of Warwick, the "kingmaker," to whom Kenilworth once belonged and from the stories he already knew, he would spin out tales of his own that lifted him to glorious heights of fantasy.

Returning home, he would come down to earth. Of what use were these dreams, these stories, these pictures and songs if his future lay in glove-making?

The thought of spending the rest of his life in the shop was bitter to him. He respected people who worked with their hands but for such things he had no skill.

That same year his brother Edmund was born. What would ordinarily have been an event of great joy brought only new worries, for here was another mouth to feed. By 1580 John Shakespeare was forced to sell off two pieces of land in Snitterfield, mortgage the great property of Asbies and rent most of it to men luckier than himself.

"Ah, Will." His father was despondent. "With Asbies clear in title, I could have asked for my coat of arms. You must have land to back up your claim to the title of gentleman, and I wanted that title so much for my sons."

"You mustn't worry about that for my sake," Will said gently, knowing that the absence of the title was not as important as the loss of the money that Asbies could have brought in. He also knew that the poorer the Shakespeares became, the less chance he had of doing anything but serving apprenticeships either to his father or to someone else in Stratford. The conflict between some bright future and the need to earn a few shillings was almost more than he could bear.

One day his father sent him to collect some money from Richard Hathaway in Shottery. Farmer Hathaway was an old family friend, but it had been nearly a year since Will had visited there. He welcomed the walk of several miles, because the sun was shining, the air was fresh and clean and he was free. As he approached the farmhouse, he noted with delight the fresh, thick, yellow thatch on the roof and summer flowers making wide bands and circles of gay colors against the green grass.

At the gate Anne Hathaway saw him coming and was astonished. Older than Will, she had always thought of him as a boy, but now she saw a young and handsome man.

"Welcome," she said. "We have not seen you for a while."

"We are working hard these days," he replied, smiling at her. "My good mother asked me to be sure to ask you to come and see the new baby. Why do we never see you in Stratford?"

She turned her pretty face away but not before he saw the unhappiness in her eyes. He knew he had been tactless.

Anne, the oldest of the Hathaway children, had become responsible for her brother Bartholomew and her sister Catherine after her mother died. Other girls married—girls not half as pretty as she—but she must stay with her father, who had married a widow who brought her own large family of children into the cottage. Anne should have been free to see young people her own age but instead her stepmother heaped more work on Anne's shoulders.

Anne and Will walked together up the path to the house. For something to say, Will remarked on the garden. "It's so pretty. Are you the gardener?"

She blushed, and when she did so Will thought she was lovely. The pink colored her clear, fine skin and made her eyes deepen to violet. "Yes. My stepmother says I spend too much time on it but I like to. Gillyflowers, primroses, columbines," she chanted, pointing to one after another, "daisies and——"

"Anne!" a voice called from the house.

All that was tender and protective and romantic in William Shakespeare rose in outrage at the way Anne stopped smiling, and hurriedly ran into the house.

Joan Hathaway was no ogre. Actually she was a hardworking woman whose only fault was that she cared more for her own children than she did for Anne's comfort and spared the girl no more than she did herself, tending the farm. But to Will she was a cruel stepmother and Anne a princess turned into a slave. As he followed, he wondered why he had never noticed before how pretty Anne was.

Mistress Hathaway directed Will to the fields, when he asked

30

for her husband. She was busy, curt, and Will saw it as bad temper. As he headed toward Richard Hathaway who was cutting hay, he thought again of poor, sweet Anne having to live with such a woman.

"I know why you've come, Will." The farmer wiped the sweat off his face. "It's the debt I owe your father. I have part of the money put by. Wait until I have finished this bit and we'll go into the house. You'll stay for supper with us."

It was a big family that crowded the Hathaway table for supper. There was little conversation; they were too hungry to talk. Afterward Will would have left for home but Hathaway pressed him to stay. "It's early yet. Sit for a while and tell us the news of Stratford."

So Will told them the news, then Richard Hathaway held them all spellbound with tales about witches and elves, about Boneless who came to naughty children, about fairy god-mothers who watched over orphans.

"Though it's summer, there's a chill in the air, Father," Anne interrupted. "Shall I make a fire?"

"Aye, lass. Let Bart help you."

But it was Will who carried in the wood for her and built the fire. Her eyes thanked him with such warmth, her soft mouth smiled so sweetly at him, that he was suddenly caught up in wonderment at this new feeling he had for her.

When it was time for Will to leave they urged him to come back soon and he said he would. Anne lit the candle to show him to the door, and smiled at him as he looked back from the gate. It was her face—not the fairies—that bewitched him as he went through the clearing in the woods.

From then on he spent every spare moment he could at the Hathaway cottage, partly because he was young and romantic, partly because the farmhouse was cheerful and his own was not. The Hathaways loved the stories he told from *The Palace of Pleasure*, a book by William Painter, left by a London merchant who had visited the Shakespeares' home. He enthralled them with stories of knights and fair ladies, of strange journeys taken to fulfill vows or avenge honor, of brothers lost at birth and finding each other again.

From another book, Will read them other tales—of a rich heiress whose husband would be the one of her suitors who picked the right casket of three: one of gold, one of silver and one of lead; of a merchant who almost had to give a pound of his flesh to a creditor, and was saved by a clever lawyer.

"Ah, that was a strange tale, that was," Hathaway exclaimed. "Those Italians, what droll ways they have. Wife, where is the lute? Will can play us a tune and Anne will sing a ballad."

They were sitting out in the garden on benches and on the grass. Joan Hathaway left the garden, where they were all sitting, to fetch the lute and her husband managed to get the children out of the way. He had seen how it was with his daughter and young Shakespeare and he approved.

"Did you like the tale, Anne?" Will rolled over on the grass and looked up into her face.

"Oh, I did. But it doesn't seem as if they were real people, these wealthy lords and ladies."

"Would you like to be wealthy and visit great cities and live in them, Anne?"

"No, I think not. I would be frightened. I would never want to leave Shottery and Stratford. I don't like strange customs and strange ways."

He sighed. "I would."

"I would be sorry to see you go." Then she blushed. She looked so beautiful in the soft twilight that Will was absolutely giddy, just looking at her.

The Hathaways came back and brought the lute. Will played country airs and Anne sang songs of love and romance. When he left that night Will knew he was in love.

For the next months he saw Anne as often as he could. He did all the foolish, poetic, silly things that lovers will do—he polished his boots until he almost wore through the leather; he combed his hair ten times a day to smooth the slight natural curl out of it; he wore his best velvet hat when he went to Shottery, even on weekdays; he carved Anne's name on the trunks of trees and composed countless poems and sonnets to her.

Gentle and quiet in his outward manner, Will Shakespeare was ardent, fiery and passionate in his true nature. His mother and father tried to reason him out of this romance, telling him that he was too young, that Anne was older than he; that he could not afford to think of marriage just now.

Marriage? Will was not exactly thinking about that. He was in love with love, with the intoxicating way that Anne looked at him. At the demure way she held her head; at the pretty way she blushed.

Without warning, the hearty, brawny Richard Hathaway took sick and died. Almost immediately the eldest son Bartholomew married and moved away, leaving the property in the widow's hands. Anne could stay if she wanted to, and work for her board, but she was unprotected, without rights or property.

To Will, it was intolerable that Anne should lose her rightful inheritance and be condemned to a life of drudgery. Everything that was generous and tender in him made him yearn to rescue her. He shut his ears to reasonable arguments and they ran away to the diocese of the Bishop of Worcester and were married. The year was 1582. He was eighteen and she was twenty-six.

They came home to Stratford and the Shakespeare house on a bitterly cold night. Will lifted the latch and ushered his bride into his home.

His mother knew immediately what had happened, but no dismay showed on her face as she took her daughter-in-law into her arms and welcomed her.

"Come in, Anne. My blessings on you both. Come, sit by the fire and be warm. Gilbert, take Anne's chest and bundles up to the room you share with Will and move your own clothes into the room where Richard sleeps." She sighed once and was again her usual calm and pleasant self. "Well, it's done. Anne, you will be as my own daughter to me. Your father is working late, Will. Go to him and tell him—he was worried greatly as to your whereabouts today."

33

Will passed through the door that divided the living quarters from the glove shop, and found his father seated at a bench, working by candlelight. To keep warm John Shakespeare had covered his shoulders with the rich velvet cloak he usually wore only to preside at council meetings; its fur collar was drawn tightly around his neck. Somehow the mantle made him look forbidding and unapproachable. Will felt a little frightened.

"I know. I know all about it." His father waved away Will's attempt to tell him of the marriage. "I heard the commotion through the door. Sit down, William. We will speak further tomorrow, but tonight I must speak seriously to you in private. I won't pretend: I wish you had waited. But Anne is a fine woman, the daughter of an old friend. And it is done."

He put down the knife and looked squarely at his son. "You have come into a man's estate and are now responsible for a wife and the children that will come. There will be no more holidays, no more dreaming in the forests or on the banks of the Avon. Gilbert has been helping me in the shop and shows a talent for it, which you do not. The shop cannot support us all. Therefore you must find work that will bring in more money. You are married now and must make your own way."

He smiled slightly at the stunned look on Will's face. "What? Did you think that you and the pretty Anne were going to stroll hand in hand through life, singing to the lute and being fed and clothed by the elves?"

"No, of course not," Will said in a low voice.

John Shakespeare put aside his work and took off his cloak. "Come, I did not mean for you to be unhappy on your wedding night. We will go and join the others. It's not often these days we have wine, but I have saved a bottle for just such a special occasion."

He went out. It was a few seconds before Will followed him.

When he left the shop, his boyhood was behind him. Setting aside the sweet and foolish nonsense of his courtship, he took up the sober responsibilities of a husband.

4

It was true that the glove shop could not support the entire Shakespeare family, so Will set out to find work. First he became an assistant to a country schoolteacher, and for a while it seemed good to be back in the world of Latin and Greek. But his main job was to keep order and discipline, and he hated it. The kindness of his own parents had instilled in him a fierce hatred of the cruelty to children which was then taken for granted, and he could hardly bring himself to cane an unruly boy. Luckily for him, the job paid so little that he was able to give it up when another and better opportunity came along.

The new position was as clerk to Henry Rogers, the Stratford lawyer. It afforded Will a splendid chance to study and learn the law while earning a few shillings a week copying briefs and doing any odd jobs Rogers wanted. Lawyers were important, lawyers became rich. Will Shakespeare would be a lawyer.

He found the learning of it easy. Rogers was astonished at the quickness of mind and the astounding memory of young Shakespeare, who could read a lawbook and grasp its contents faster than he himself could read a chapter. The apprentice came to work early every morning and all day was swallowed up in the legal atmosphere of the office, absorbing the language, the rules, the minute details involved in vouchers, inheritances, wills, complaints. And slowly Will grew to loathe it.

Outside his office window, life was being lived in all its lustiness while he was entombed inside, amid crackling papers and deed boxes. Outside there was the chatter of the marketplace, the laughter and talk of the women as they washed clothes at the town pump, the clatter of horses' hoofs on the cobbled street. There were travelers from London rattling into the courtyard of the Bull Inn, handing their tired horses over to the ostler and stopping for a moment outdoors to chat with the innkeeper. Only the merest breath of life in busy Stratford entered the stuffy office where Will was bent over quill and paper.

Occasionally those papers came to life when Rogers let him question plaintiffs, defendants or witnesses in a legal case. He was stirred by the true stories they told him, stories as thrilling as the ones he used to make up—tales of murder for honor or passion, of crimes committed out of desperate need. Will's sympathies were aroused by the plight of the tragic or unfortunate people who came to the law office. It was their emotions and fears, their hates and loves, their tragedy and suffering that alone interested him.

Rogers shook his head. "There's little money in such, Will. Turn your thoughts to mortgages and property disputes or inheritance entails. That's where the money is."

Will did his best. Certainly the little money he earned was desperately needed at home. He was aware that the promise of his someday becoming a lawyer kept the hope of a better future for them all alive in his father's heart. He stuck to his job and also let it be known in Stratford that he was available for odd jobs after work. He was not too proud to do anything, even to help the butcher slaughter cattle, the worst possible job for a man who hated killing.

Will might not have been so unhappy if he and Anne could have kept a private, secret world of romance for themselves, but they had to live in the crowded Henley Street home. And now that she was married, Anne took pride in copying the dignified behavior of her mother-in-law. Quickly she had lost the girlish, naïve quality that Will had found so enchanting. She worried about Will, who was getting too thin, working too hard, taking his responsibilities too seriously. He worried about her, regretting that he had plunged into marriage when he could not offer a wife a house of her own.

Occasionally the pressure was too much; he was young and something wild in him broke loose. At those times he would join the other daredevils of the town to hunt Sir Thomas Lucy's deer at night. They were finally caught, and Sir Thomas, who was High Sheriff, threatened to punish them severely. The young scamps were let off with a heavy fine, which rankled Will's pride. Out of sheer bravado he wrote a verse and tacked it up on Sir Lucy's gate:

> A parliament Member, a justice of peace
> At home a poor scarecrow, at London an ass
> If Lousy is Lucy, as some folk miscall it
> Then Lucy is lousy, whatever befall it
> He thinks himself great, yet an ass in his state
> We allow by his ears but with asses to mate
> If Lucy is lousy, as some folk miscall it
> Sing Lousy Lucy, whatever befall it.

Such reckless moods and deeds always passed quickly, after which he would work harder than ever. Frustration continued to burn inside him but he kept it hidden as best he could.

Sometimes in the evening he would coax Anne to stroll with him through the orchards and gardens down to the banks of the Avon. Although she loved him dearly, she could listen for only a little while to the dreams and hopes he poured out to her, then she grew impatient to be back in the house helping Mary Shakespeare with the spinning, the sewing, the mending. She had to be practical. A child was on the way.

Their daughter, Susanna, was born the next year, 1583.

Will gained a child whom he adored, but he lost forever the sweetheart in Anne. She had been young for her age when he married her, but in motherhood maturity caught up with her. She no longer blushed or dimpled when he teased her, there was a lovely dignity to her, but he missed the other Anne.

It was in this mood of discontent that Will received a letter from Richard Field in London. His old friend wrote:

How can you stay and rot in Stratford? London is the greatest city you can imagine. Our company is so rushed with business that Master Vautrollier is printing night and day and says he has never seen such an appetite of people for anything printed, be it book, play, poem, ballad, song, tract or pamphlet. I have heard that you are studying the law. Here, in the law courts of Gray's Inn or Lincoln's Inn or the Middle Temple, you could surely find employment. The young gentlemen-nobles who study there have no desire to become lawyers; they merely further their education . . .

Will had gone to the orchard to read his letter in privacy. Pausing now, he leaned back against the heavy trunk of an apple tree and closed his eyes. The longing in him for a wider, more exciting world than Stratford was so overwhelming that he had to fight down the impulse to rush off. He could not go. It was his duty to remain.

After a while he read on:

I am sending you two books. One is a poem by Edmund Spenser, *The Shepheardes Calender*. The other is a translation by Sir Thomas North of Plutarch's *Lives* and is called *Lives of the Noble Grecians and Romans*. And I must tell you of a strange new way of writing which has infected all the noblemen who like to boast they can write a sonnet as easily as they can fight with a rapier. It has been dubbed euphuism, from a tale of *Euphues* by one John Lyly. He is the son of the Lyly who wrote our Latin Grammar we studied in school. The trick of euphuism is that you must never say plainly what you mean but must wind it and twist it and elaborate it.

That night Will answered the letter, begging Richard to write more often. Then he lost himself in Spenser's beautiful poem and went to bed. He lay awake for hours repeating the verses and making up his own.

Matters did not improve for the Shakespeare family. When

in 1584 twin children were born to Will and Anne, Hamnet, the boy, and Judith, the girl, it became more of a struggle for Will and his father to feed so many.

As the next two years went by, Will felt caught in a prison, doing endless drudgery at jobs he hated. He loved his whole family, but he was hemmed in, frustrated that he could not fulfill the great need they had of him.

Richard's infrequent letters were both a delight and a torment. Holinshed's *Chronicles of England, Scotland and Ireland* which Richard sent Will, excited him greatly for here was the whole history of his country, not just the little bit which was legend in Warwickshire. From king to king, war to war, he read about all of England's past—the betrayals, the conquests, the exalted deeds of honorable men and the treacheries of villains.

In April of 1587 Richard wrote:

> You cannot imagine how London is growing, Will. It has doubled in size since I came here. Our overseas trade brings in great wealth and every master of every trade is adding new apprentices . . . There is every chance for success here. Do you recall our meeting with the play actors that day? I sometimes go to Burbage's Theatre, but not often because I am busy. All of London has gone mad over playhouses . . . Not many call the players vagabonds now. Her Majesty has seen fit to set her approval on them by selecting a company to bear her own name, the Queen's Men, and to wear her livery. I do urge you, Will, to come to London and employ yourself in the courts of law here. Besides the pleasure it would give me to see you again, it would surely be advantageous to you.

This time, temptation would not be silenced by reason or duty. Instead, Will asked himself: Why not? It would be a long time before he could call himself a lawyer and even then there might not be enough practice to keep him and the other lawyers in Stratford busy.

Going to the window in Rogers' law office, Will looked out. The town was growing, a few new houses were being built—but oh, so slowly compared to London. Down the street a trumpet blared. He smiled. In Richard's letter he had just read about the actors and here they were again coming into Stratford. Now the trumpet was louder and nearer; he could hear a drum beating too. He leaned out of the window to get a better view of the troupe coming down the street. Yes, they were the Earl of Leicester's men.

An idea sprang into Will's mind, startling, sudden, but as completely formed as if he had thought it out slowly and carefully. He ran out of the office and hastened along the street to the inn. As he entered, a stout actor was just raising a tankard of ale to his lips and he spilled part of it as Will's voice came unexpectedly from behind:

"Is there a Master Burbage with you today?"

The man lowered his tankard and looked around. "Why do you ask for Burbage? My name is Kempe, William Kempe. At your service. No, Burbage stays in London. He has been chosen for the Queen's Men and is one of her pets, while we wander the byways and highways for our audiences. What did you want with him?"

"Are you going to London?"

"We are, in time. First to Oxford——"

"Will you take me with you?"

"For safety? True, it's best to travel with a group, for you'll find thieves everywhere who'll gladly cut your throat to steal your purse and horse. But you'd make better time by finding a train of merchants to travel with. We go slowly."

Will shook his head. Now that the words had actually been said, his mind was made up. A sudden notion had crystallized into decision. "Nay, you do not understand, sir. I have no money. I thought perhaps I could work for my passage to London with you—surely there is something I can do? I am not proud. I will do anything."

Another man came over to Kempe while young Shakespeare was talking, and the two actors stared at him for several minutes. Just as Will thought he could stand their silence no longer, the men glanced at each other and a slight nod passed between them. Then Kempe, gulping the last of his ale, said, "Come upstairs with us. It's too noisy to talk here."

He led the way out of the crowded tavern room, crossed over to the other side of the stone-paved courtyard and climbed the steps that led to the private rooms. Only when they were inside and Kempe had settled himself comfortably did he speak again:

"Now then, can you act?"

"Act?" Will had never even thought of that. He had meant to work *for* them, not *with* them. "I could but try, sir."

"We need someone to take a small part now and then, just to speak a line or two. We have all been doubling up in parts, but it is inconvenient and often requires too quick a change of costumes."

"When you aren't acting," the other man said, "you could use the prompt book, which means that you stand just offstage and give us the cue when we are to speak. If a man forgets his lines, you prompt him." He smiled. "My name is Tarleton, Richard Tarleton. We do not yet know yours, young man."

"William Shakespeare."

"Do you know anything that you can recite for us?"

Thousands of words of poetry and prose tumbled through Will's head, but he chose a stanza from Spenser's *Shepheardes Calender*. He spoke the lines but it seemed to him that none of this was real, that he was not standing there reciting poetry for these two players. It could not actually be happening to him.

"Excellent!" Tarleton exclaimed when Will had finished. "You have a true musical pitch of voice and fine expression. To have remembered that you must be in the habit of memorizing —which is necessary in our profession."

The stout Kempe leaned forward, his hands on his knees. "Are you serious about wanting to go with us? If so, we can use you. It is not our custom to pick up a stranger with no training, but we have need of someone. We wanted to be sure about your voice and to see that you did not stumble or stammer or blush while speaking. We can teach you the tricks of acting—

41

how to strut, how to rave in anger, how to brandish a sword, how to weep and to laugh—but you have the voice already, as well as a fine appearance."

Tarleton, meanwhile, was examining him critically. "He would be ideal in the role of a young prince or a nobleman, with his fine, high forehead and rather lofty manner. He's much too sensitive-looking to play a clown or a rustic. How old are you, William?"

"I was twenty-three this month." Will spoke mechanically, his mind in a daze.

"Then it is settled." Kempe arose. "We play here this afternoon, then tomorrow make for Oxford, thence on to London, playing in whatever towns will guarantee us a crowd. Be ready to leave with us at dawn. Mind, though, we can pay you nothing but your food and lodging."

Thus, so quickly, was Will's fate decided.

5

At six o'clock the next morning Will Shakespeare left the house in Henley Street, pausing only to tousle Gilbert's hair and then listen to his mother's whispered good-byes. She fussed a little over him, seeing to it that he was wearing his linen collar and that his one white ruff was tucked away in his leather bag, along with his best cap, a change of shirts, his grandfather's best blue silk cape. At his side she buckled on the Arden sword his aunts had given him on his sixteenth birthday.

Anne still slept. She had been up until two o'clock washing and pleating and starching and ironing and sewing his white ruff. Will did not awaken her to say good-by, only looked at her with quiet affection and murmured, "My true and honorable wife." Then he stopped to kiss the soft cheeks of the babies in their truckle beds.

"Good-by, Will," his mother said at the doorway. "Do not fret over the harsh words spoken last night, nor the tears. No one meant them—it is only that you astonished us and your father is afraid for you in the city. No one thinks you go to escape your obligations. And your father bade me give you these." She handed Will a newly sewn pair of gloves, beautiful in their workmanship. "He had made them for one of the squires at Kenilworth, but he wants you to have them."

Will's resolution almost weakened at this proof of his father's love, in spite of the bitter reproaches he had uttered last night.

Mary Shakespeare saw her son's face soften, and her own became firm. "Nay, Will, you must go. My heart has ached, watching you toil here with no future. With your wit and learn-

43

ing and Richard Field as a friend, you will make your fortune in London. You will not forget us. Though she cried last night, Anne knows that well."

He held her close. "Good-by, sweet lady mother," he said, kissing her. Then he was off.

"Ah, Will. You are ready?" Richard Tarleton hailed him from the courtyard. "Come quickly then. The horses stand ready to be mounted."

The great adventure was about to begin.

The troupe galloped out of the innyard, crossed the many-arched stone bridge over the Avon and then rode swiftly at a steady pace so that the night would see them in Oxford. It was a long, hard ride with only a brief pause at a farmhouse to buy apples and milk. Then they were off again, with Shakespeare feeling greater release and freedom with each mile put between himself and Stratford.

It was not pitch dark when they came out of the Forest of Shotover, yet there were lights in the town windows down in the plains. As they drew nearer, Will strained to see the outlines of the university spires and towers against the starry sky.

They arrived at the inn hungry and tired. Will stopped to wash his face at the pump and comb his hair, then gratefully entered the big, dark room with its high timbered ceiling, its long tables covered with leather-jack tankards and wooden plates. Gladly he sat down, his nose twitching at the delightful aroma of roast capon and steaming mutton broth and freshly baked bread.

The players ate in silence, but once filled, they leaned back on their benches, braced against the wall, and began to talk. One called for the tapster to bring them sack and sherry; another brought out dice from his pocket.

"Come on, young Stratford," they called to Will, "throw a dice with us."

He refused politely, and when they would have insisted, Tarleton stopped them. "Leave be. He must read the play and study it or he will not be able to prompt you in your lines tomorrow

44

or speak his own." Seating himself beside Will, he called for candles and unrolled the long sheets of manuscript.

Will was glad for this occupation. It was not that he did not care for games; he and his family had played at cards or tenpins. But he had too few shillings to risk. Besides, he was too excited, even though he tried hard to keep it from showing in his face. He could hardly concentrate on the script before him because he kept looking up to be sure he was not missing anything.

There was much to see and watch and hear. In one corner was an enormously fat man who drank more than Will had ever believed was possible, yet it did not dim the man's spirits or his nimble wits as he played tricks on his companions and teased the barmaids.

In another corner were three merchants, arguing, buying and selling, trying to outdo each other. When four students came in, Will smiled to himself at the contrast between their shabby clothes and their peacock manners. How haughty they looked, and how crestfallen when the maid called them "boys."

Will read until his eyes ached and he was certain that he knew the play, then he wandered out into the town. It was very late but he was too excited to sleep.

Here were the streets he had once hoped to walk as a student. Those were the colleges, with their libraries and chapels, where he had once wanted to be. Now there were no bitter regrets—he was on his way to London.

The next morning Kempe coached him in the few lines he would have to speak. Then the two of them stepped into the courtyard where the play would be given.

The three-storied inn, with the tavern in one corner, and a huge gated entrance formed a hollow square. All the bedrooms could be reached from the courtyard by outside stairs, so that a man could dismount and go to his room without ever setting foot in the tavern. Each story had a balcony running along all three sides.

In these balconies benches and chairs were being placed so that those who could afford it sat there, leaning over the railings

45

to see the stage below. Horses and wagons and carts had been cleared out of the yard and the inn servants were helping to erect a temporary stage that projected into the middle of the court-yard. Those who could only pay a penny stood in the yard itself.

The innkeeper, of course, was happy. Plays always drew large crowds, and he would sell ale and beer the whole time the per-formance was on. By two o'clock the yard and the balconies were filled and the play began.

When it was Will's turn to go onstage he walked out without any fear and spoke well. But in the third act he faced Will Kempe, opened his mouth—and nothing came out. He could not remember a single word! His throat was paralyzed, his mind completely numbed. What was he doing here on this stage? Why were all those people staring at him?

Kempe went right on talking, complete master of the situa-tion, making up lines and pretending that Will's silence was part of the play. But he maneuvered himself so that his back was to the audience and he looked straight at Will. There was no mistaking the command flashed from his eyes. Behind him Will suddenly heard his cue whispered to him by the prompt man.

The words all came back to him in a rush and his panic left him. He spoke his lines, completing his small speech without further mishap, then bowed as he had been instructed to do, and backed off the stage.

Afterward Kempe laughed away Will's apologies. "It happens to all of us, including professional actors. I have seen men run off the stage and refuse to come back—such people can never become actors. You didn't run. You came to your senses and remembered your lines; I'm proud of you. In the first act you spoke very well—I couldn't have put more feeling in it myself."

From that moment on, acting fascinated Will. He watched the way the others used their hands, the way they stood and walked, the way they raised or lowered their voices and yet made themselves heard in the farthest part of the yard and up in the balconies. He saw an actor cry real tears in a death scene; another could laugh and have the whole audience laughing with him.

In Kempe and Tarleton he recognized true genius. Both had been on the stage most of their lives and were famous throughout England for their clowning. Tarleton could make up jokes as he went along, and often engaged in a battle of wits with the audience, letting them heckle him so he could throw back humorous quips. Kempe was the master of comic faces. And both men excelled in the jig, a sort of lyrical farce which was sung and danced to as a ballad.

Both men liked William Shakespeare's gentle manners, which somehow intensified their impression that beneath his exterior lay a searching, eager mind and an ardent nature. They liked his amazing capacity for hard work and hard study, which made them all the more willing to coach him in his small parts.

Will was learning the trade of acting, but at the same time he was doing something else: studying human nature. From behind the curtain where he sat with his prompt book he watched the people in the audience. For him they were never just a faceless blur of spectators. They were individuals, and their stories could be read in their faces.

The vitality in Will which for years had been like a dammed-up stream was now released in a joyful surge that swept through his whole body, making all his senses come alive. He exulted in the hard pounding of the horse beneath him. He listened, marveling at the different accents of English voices from one shire to the next. At night he could hardly sleep, for his mind was crowded with vivid pictures of a great cathedral in a town, of a milkmaid waving to them from a barn door, of the slow wagons they had passed in one mile and the richly dressed entourage of a nobleman that had thundered past them the next mile, of a parson on a mule, reading his Bible as he jogged along.

With this great upsurge of feeling came an unblocking of poetry, songs and words in his mind. He kept these secret, fearing to be laughed at.

Through High Wycombe, through Beaconsfield, along Uxbridge Road they came to Shepherd's Bush, and then one cool, dull, cloudy day they rode into London Town.

6

Will's heart was hammering in his breast. The very word "London" seemed to quicken his blood and he felt warm in spite of the wind that whipped at his clothes. It was impossible to conceal his impatience and excitement any longer.

"Is this the City?" he asked Kempe.

"Not yet."

When the chimneypots multiplied into hundreds and houses were joined one to another, with shops sprinkled among them, he thought they surely must be there.

But—"Not yet," laughed Kempe.

Then they came to Aldersgate and when they passed through it, they were actually in London and Will did not need to ask. His own dazzled eyes told him they had at last arrived.

It seemed impossible that there could be so many people, so many houses, so much commotion, with the narrow streets bursting and pulling the houses and walls down upon them. Cries resounded in his ears: hawkers shouting, music coming from somewhere, people talking, calling to one another. His eyes could not take in all he saw and, numbed, he followed the horse in front of him as the troupe forced their way through the crowds, crying out, "Make way!"

Will had a sudden shock: Why, the houses seldom had a garden between them! They were shoulder to shoulder and the upper stories were built out over the lower ones so that Will felt he could lean from his horse and pick a flower from a pot on the sill of a second-story window.

Shop after shop, booth after booth, houses and more houses, church spires on every corner—everywhere he looked there was a tangle of streets and lanes, inner courts or market places, alleys that twisted and curved and twined.

London people walked fast and spoke fast. Boys darted around the horses' legs; a baker went by with a tray of loaves on his head; men crossed the street, angrily demanding that the troupe hold back and let them by. Women walked close to the shops to avoid being splashed with mud, or were carried by servants in sedan chairs. There was such a busy, lively, bustling air about London that he had not seen anywhere else. It bewildered him, but it also excited him.

But there were ghastly and horrible things too. Around Aldersgate, Will had caught a fearful glimpse of several heads of criminals rotting on posts. London could be cruel, dirty, evil-smelling. In the heart of London, the stench was just as bad. The only sewers were ditches that sluggishly carried debris down the sides of the streets. Will was filled with horror at the sight of filthy beggars and children whose faces were scarred by the marks of the pox.

Kempe finally halted in front of a boardinghouse that he had recommended to Will for its cheapness. As the weary young actor slid off his horse and unhitched his leather bag from the saddle, Kempe leaned over to speak to him:

"Stay here, Will, so's I may find you. Your friend Field may have work for you and again he may not. When we've settled where we're to play in London and what we will do, I'll try to get a role for you if you want it. I won't forget you, Will."

"My gratitude to you, sir," Will answered.

When they were gone Will knocked at the door of the narrow, ugly house. The woman who opened it was as narrow and ugly as the house, and the smell of rancid food, spilled ale and year-old floor rushes assailed his nostrils. With sinking heart he followed her up to a gloomy attic room. All it contained was a bag of straw on the floor for a bed, a small table and a stool, and it was grimy and dank—but he took it because that was all he could afford. After bargaining with the woman for lodgings and laundry, he inquired the way of her to St. Paul's.

"Be careful that you are back before nightfall," the woman warned him. "The town is full of pickpockets and thieves and you are not armed."

Heeding her words, Will buckled on his grandfather's sword after she left. He thought it looked very well with his long blue cloak and the white ruff Anne had made for him. Thinking of her and his family, Will was suddenly homesick, but he told himself that it was the ugly room that dampened his spirits.

Once outside on the street, he regained his buoyant spirits. He was in London, no mistake about that.

He was about to cross a street when he was crowded to the wall by a pageboy running down the street, elbowing people out of the way and calling, "Way! Make way for my Lady!"

Will stopped to stare at a sedan chair that followed, carried by two stalwart men in scarlet livery. But it was not the stiff spreading satin skirts of the lady, nor her high, white, lace-encrusted ruff, nor the splendid black fan she waved back and forth, nor even the tiny black mask she wore, that made him gape. She was painted! Two round orange spots flamed on her cheeks, and, countryman though he was, he knew it could not be natural.

"Watch where you're going, there." A sailor, with hoops of gold in his ears and a yellow bandana around his head, caught Will's arm. "Don't be bumping into a man, like that."

"I beg your pardon. I wasn't looking where I was going."

"And where are ye going?"

"To St. Paul's Cathedral," Will told him.

"And there it be, right before your eyes." The sailor pointed and Will had his first glimpse of the great cathedral.

Not quite believing his eyes, he approached the front of the church. Accustomed to the quiet serenity of Trinity Church in Stratford, he was appalled to see the courtyard swarming with booths and stalls of all kinds where venders cried out over the rest of the din to come buy their wares. Here men loitered when they had nothing better to do, or wrote their names and ages on bills, which they posted over their heads so that a master might read and give them a job. Here Londoners met to keep appointments or settle matters of business.

Will walked through the noisy, pushing crowds, shocked by the sacrilege of trade and flippant talk which almost drowned out the faint sounds of the choir singing from the cathedral.

Inside, however, matters were even worse. Down in front a choir sang; a preacher preached. But the back of the church was entirely given over to business, with stalls for selling. Money changed hands briskly over the counters; lawyers lounged against pillars and interviewed clients; well-dressed gentlemen strolled up and down the aisles.

Will was so disturbed he walked out. Passing a stall near the bottom of the cathedral steps where there was a counter of printed matter, he moved toward it and spied a familiar figure.

"Richard! Ho!" he called.

A portly, substantial man of business turned and in his fleshy face Will saw all that was left of the sixteen-year-old lad he once had known—the friendly, honest eyes.

"Will! Is it really you? When did you come to London?"

"This very day, not two hours ago." While recounting his decision to leave Stratford and his encounter with the actors, Will took stock of his friend. Richard Field had certainly changed in appearance. He had assumed the airs of a much older man, and there was a shrewd look about him. But he was genuinely glad to see Will and clapped him on the arm.

"We must see what can be done for you. If you can get temporary work with these actors, I would advise you to do so— then we will have time to look about for an advantageous opening, either in the law courts or with the printers. You would not want to work for me; you would have to start with apprentices half your age."

"Does Master Vautrollier employ so many?"

Richard looked at him with surprise. "I forgot that the news would not yet have reached Stratford before you left. Vautrollier died—God keep him. I married his widow and now control the company. It is Richard Field, Stationer, now."

So that explained the airs and the self-importance—but Will did not begrudge him success. However, he felt that it created a barrier between them. Richard was established, wealthy, while he was a penniless nobody, a man with a family and no work.

If his friend felt any of this, he gave no sign of it. "Come, Will, we have time for a stroll before it gets dark. Have you seen the Thames yet? No? Then you have not seen the best of London. We'll make a wide circle and I'll show you the Tower of London first."

"But can you leave the stall?"

"My clerks will attend to it. I am rarely here. Most times you will find me at the printing shop." He fell into step with Will, guiding him to the left of the cathedral. He asked for news of the Shakespeares, the Fields and others in Stratford, and when he had heard all that Will could tell him, he spoke about his own affairs.

"If more people could read and write, we would double and treble the sale of books. There is such a hunger to know and learn—that is why they flock to the plays, Will. That's where they find out what is happening at court or in foreign lands."

Long before they reached it Will could see the Tower of London and its gray stone walls and keeps. The mighty fortress was surrounded by its own high walls.

"But it's not only a fortress," Richard explained. "It is also a place where noble prisoners are kept and executed."

"I know. We also heard in Stratford that Mary Stuart was executed at Fotheringlyhay Castle. A pity—a tragedy."

"Ah, Will, you do not like these religious and political quarrels that divide families. I have not forgotten what you once said to me. But, my friend, there could not be two queens in England, even if one was in prison. As long as Catholic Mary was alive, she was the focus for conspiracy. Our enemies abroad, the Duke of Guise in France and Philip in Spain, found justification for their dreams of conquering England by upholding Mary's right to the throne. It had to be done, yet Elizabeth put it off these many years until last February—and only then because she was forced to it by Cecil, her chief adviser."

"Were matters so desperate?" Will asked moodily.

"Desperate? Think you there is no danger of war? Why, Will, we are perilously close to it. The Spanish have overrun the Netherlands; Henry III of France has sided with Spain. It is not to save the Netherlands but to save England that we are building ships of war right now. Five thousand of our soldiers have been sent to Antwerp. Sir Francis Drake has been given a free hand to attack Spanish ships and imprison their crews wherever he may find them. Have you not heard of the Armada?"

"Kempe mentioned it. The Earl of Leicester took him to Antwerp last year to provide entertainment between battles. He merely said that the Spaniards were building a monstrous fleet, but I thought they were to attack the Netherlands——"

"No. To attack us!"

Their conversation was interrupted, for they had circled the Tower and come out upon the Thames.

Nothing Will had seen so far captured his fancy as did this river. For the moment he could think of nothing else and Richard, remembering his own first sight of it, was silent.

It was almost as busy as the streets. Threading their way along its smooth gray waters were brightly painted boats—wherries, punts, barges, sailboats, brown-sailed trading vessels. People crowded the steps of the wharfs, waiting to be carried to the other side. Looking across, Will saw that there were fewer houses and many more fields and orchards than on this side.

The air here smelled good to him. He did not mind the river odors of water-soaked wood and pitchy oakum, tar and resin. Nearby was a ship and he got a whiff of its cargo of sweet, cinnamony spices.

It was a noisy, colorful scene. The watermen—Richard said there were thousands of them—called profane greetings to one another as their boats passed, or else they lined the stone steps yelling the price of fares to passengers. There was but one bridge across the Thames, London Bridge, and Will could see it in the distance. The two friends continued along the bank, past the Customs House, and, just before the bridge, came to a place that Richard said was called Billingsgate. As they passed it Will heard music.

"Is there a show of some kind where they have musicians?"

Richard laughed. "It is only a barbershop. Rich customers demand music while they are being shaved or having their hair cut, and so each barber prides himself on having the best flute or the best piper or the best viol in the City. Come, let us go and rest a while." Just beyond London Bridge he halted in front of a large and handsome tavern with the sign, THE THREE CRANES IN VINTRY.

They chose a table by the window and Richard ordered for both of them. Will looked across the river to the other side.

"What is the name of that large church?"

"St. Mary in Overy. And not far away, almost across from it, is the Bear Garden. It's that large, round building. You must see a bear-baiting sometime. But I advise you not to cross the river alone except in daylight. There are houses there and gardens, as you see, but there are also some pretty dangerous places because it's outside the City proper."

A half-hour passed quickly as they talked, then Richard got to his feet. "I must leave you, Will. Tomorrow evening I want you to dine with us. I would ask you tonight but my wife sets a good table and likes to have notice of guests so the cook can prepare fancy dishes. Will you walk with me?"

"No, I'll stay awhile. Thank you, Richard."

Twilight was approaching when Will emerged from the inn and went to the busy river bank. He put Richard's address safely away and set out to see more of the Thames. After a long walk, beyond Bridewell Prison, Will came upon such fine mansions and castles as he had never dreamed of seeing. Their glass windows were colored in lovely hues of rose and yellow and blue or were as clear as crystal. He stared up at their towering heights, wondering what it would be like to be inside one of them, and then laughed at himself for standing there thinking such thoughts, with scarcely a penny in his pocket.

He turned away, his head aswim with the things he had seen that day. Following Richard's directions, he easily reached his own squalid lodgings. After a poor supper, he wrote to Anne and was asleep the minute his head touched the pillow of straw.

The next day he went again to the river and this time spent two of his pennies to be ferried across. He joined a great crowd on the other side, following them to the tall, round building that Richard had called the Bear Garden. Tempted and curious, he paid another of his precious pennies to go inside.

What he saw there sickened and disgusted him, as much because of the frenzy of the audience as because of the goings-on down in the pit. A bear, chained to a stake, was being cut and ripped and tortured by cruel-fanged dogs. Sometimes the huge bear was lucky to catch one of his tormentors with a swipe of his paw and kill him. Will left before the show was halfway over, revolted by the brutality and even more by the maddened excitement and enjoyment of the spectators.

On the way out he overheard a strange conversation. Two fashionably dressed ladies, leaving at the same time he did, were loudly lamenting that they had to go before the bear was killed by the dogs. As one climbed into her sedan chair, she called to the other:

"You must come this evening, my dear. The singing master is presenting the new madrigal he has learned, and we have engaged new musicians. Tonight we will have a gittern as well as the viol and the tabor and the pipes."

Deeply puzzled by such contrasts of behavior, Will wandered about, thinking to himself that Londoners were paradoxical, appearing bloodthirsty and brutal one moment, refined and artistic the next.

Will reached the great road that ran from Canterbury, in the south of England, to London, and followed it, knowing that it would bring him back to the river. All along the way were taverns, and when he saw one sign, THE TABARD, he remembered that Will Kempe had said it was his favorite place.

The first person that Will saw upon entering the tavern garden was Kempe himself, sitting with two other men at one of the tables outside. Will hesitated, not wanting to interrupt, but just then the actor caught sight of him.

"Ho, Will! This is good luck, our meeting thus. I would have been looking for you, had you not come by so providentially. Robert, here is the man I was telling you about: Will Shakespeare. He writes a good hand—I saw a letter he wrote to his father. He would serve your turn, I am certain."

The one called Robert merely glanced up, then went on scribbling. Will was sure he had seen him before and indeed he had. This was Robert Wilson, one of the players with James Burbage that long-ago day near Wilmcote.

Kempe introduced Will to the other man, an actor named Thomas Pope. By then Wilson had finished writing and pushed his paper aside to stare hard at Will. "Can you indeed write a fair hand? Fair enough and large enough letters so that any blockhead in the company can read it? I have just finished a comedy, *Three Ladies of London*, and now must make copies for all the actors, so they may study their lines. I need help, but you would have to write fair and fast."

Will's heart leaped. Here was work to his liking. "I have been lawyer's clerk and schoolmaster. I can write plainly."

"It won't pay well, but there may be a part in it for you. If not, there will be other work. Here—copy this and let me see what you can do."

As young Shakespeare copied the lines it seemed to him that the play was only mildly amusing. It could have been much more so if Wilson had said this instead of that, if he had written wittier lines. Then he caught himself. Who was he to be criticizing a professional writer and actor—he who knew so little about either?

The author was more than satisfied with Will's handwriting

and agreed to employ him for the next two days until rehearsals started. Handed a bundle of pages to be copied, more parchment rolls and quill pens, Will was told to be at THE BELLE SAUVAGE at two o'clock two days hence.

That night William Shakespeare set out for Richard's house on feet that hardly knew the London stones and seemed to be stepping on air. One day in London and he had work! Recklessly he bought a bunch of violets from the barrow of a flower seller and then proceeded on his way, looking for the shop with a new sign over the door: RICHARD FIELD, PRINTER, STATIONER, OF THE STATIONERS' COMPANY. Like most merchants and guildsmen, Vautrollier had built his living quarters over his shop, and Richard had moved into them after his marriage to the widow.

Mistress Field's plain, cold, middle-aged face thawed with surprised pleasure as Will presented her with the violets and uttered his most courteous greeting.

"Thank you," she said. "It has been a long while since I've received a nosegay. Richard, you did not tell me your friend was such a gentleman. Now, the two of you can sit and talk while I see if the maids have supper ready."

Richard led Will into a large, square room that contained furniture of severe but handsome design. It was the first house of its kind in London that Will had been in and he looked about with some curiosity. The late Vautrollier's taste had not been for costly things but for substantial ones. The chairs were sturdy, the tables solid. A cupboard of dark oak was so massive that it held an entire dinner service of pewter cups and plates. On top of it was a large bowl of real silver. The only object in the room that looked out of place was a delicate writing table, inlaid with ivory and ornamented with beautiful gold handles on the drawers.

Richard saw his guest looking at it. "Do you like that piece? Vautrollier brought it back with him from one of his travels in Italy. He said you would not believe the marvels of workmanship in gold and porcelain and glass being done there. We owe a debt to that country, Will, so Master Vautrollier used to say.

Fifty years ago—when the richest nobles in our land were eating with their fingers and thinking more about hunting and tournaments than about a poem or a song—in Italy there was a flowering of a great and wonderful culture."

"What do you mean, Richard?"

"For one thing, artisans wrought delicate goblets and vases out of gold and silver. Men fashioned statues out of marble, built magnificent palaces and churches. Vautrollier said he felt as if he had lost his senses as he wandered about in them. He spoke of a Michelangelo and a Raphael and a Da Vinci, of poets and troubadours. Now, of course, these things are coming to England and everyone here copies Italian dress and manners. Instead of hawks and hounds, our young nobles dream of sonnets and ballads. It's good for our trade," he said, leaning back in his chair with a pompous air that made Will smile to himself.

Shakespeare then mentioned his temporary employment as a copyist and the possibility of a part for him in the new play.

"Good! That will do until we find something better."

The mistress of the house came back, keeping a stern eye on the two servants as they set their steaming platters on the table. Then she called her husband and Will to supper.

It was excellent food and there was plenty of it. Will, who was starving by this time, could barely keep up with the maids, who scurried back and forth with more and more dishes. Yet his hunger did not prevent him from carefully observing Richard and his wife, who was more than twice his friend's age. Will saw clearly that it had been a marriage of convenience, as were many marriages in those days.

"More of the roast beef, William?" Mistress Field asked. "Richard, look to his glass—it needs filling."

"The best sherry, wife?" Richard raised his eyebrows. Obviously his wife was pleased with this Stratford friend of his.

"Richard thinks me something of a Puritan," she explained to Will. "And it is true I do not hold with drunkenness. London is crowded with able-bodied men who should be at work but instead sit about all day in taverns, dicing and enjoying themselves. We are not put here to enjoy ourselves. But I am not such a Puritan as to set a miserly table."

Will smiled at her. "Why must we not enjoy life, Mistress Field? We must work, yes—but with an occasional holiday between times."

She smiled at him indulgently. "You young men are all alike. Wait until you are master of an enterprise, then you will think differently. More and more, merchants and tradesmen are becoming Puritans, then they bring order into the lives of their apprentices, even when they are not working, to be certain that their leisure is spent in prayer and godly acts—not in loose pleasures."

Will's private opinion was that such a life would not be very happy for the apprentices, but he said nothing.

"The merchants are gaining a little power in London," Richard said with satisfaction as he sliced more roast beef and took another generous helping. "The Queen looks to us now when she needs money. Her throne is no longer at the mercy of the rich nobles, who otherwise would be able to dictate their terms if she needed money from them for the army or for ships. The throne is secure now, Will. Master Vautrollier used to say that Henry the Eighth broke with Rome and the Catholic Church not so much because of any religious differences but because of his desire to have one central authority in England. Before that, any lord or duke or earl could persuade a bishop that his cause was just, raise the banner of God and Church at the head of his army and aim to make himself king."

"I do not understand such things," Will replied. "I can see into the workings of one man's mind, but not into a nation's."

When it was time to go, Richard accompanied Will to the street door. "You must come again soon," he urged. "I have seldom seen my wife take to anyone as she has to you. You have gallant ways."

7

Will spent the next day working on Robert Wilson's play, making individual copies for each actor, as he had been instructed. The following afternoon he brought the manuscripts to THE BELLE SAUVAGE, a large inn and one of the few places the City Corporation could not rule against because it was in a "liberty" or free land, even though it lay within the City itself. It accommodated few travelers, being used mostly for the performance of shows. In fact, the stage in the courtyard was a permanent structure.

Wilson liked the work Will had done, but there was no part in the play for the copyist. Instead, he again held the prompt book during rehearsals and did everything else that was asked of him, so desperately did he need the money. He helped place the four imitation trees that were supposed to represent a forest, he practiced tolling a heavy bell offstage that would come in, on cue, for the death scene. Then he was sent to the mercer's to buy lengths of cloth for costumes. He was also asked to study the lines of two of the actors in case either fell ill. For these many chores he was paid a shilling a day.

He learned that in London there were three classes of stage workers: regular actors, who sometimes shared in the profits; hirelings like himself, who acted infrequently; lastly, the servants who did the heavy jobs of repairing the stage, running errands, mending costumes, or collecting the money at the gate.

Will was glad to be with the company again. Tarleton was no longer with them, having joined the Queen's Men, but new actors had come in from whom Will felt he could learn much. Sometimes Robert Wilson would talk to him offstage as they watched a scene together.

"I've been an actor and still am, but there aren't enough plays to perform, so I've turned writer," he told Will. "The London public is like a hungry lion, swallowing up plays and wanting new ones every week. People are getting fussier too . . . Did you ever have half-eaten apples and oranges thrown in your face when you were acting, Will? It's happened to us many times. It's new and better plays they want, and there's no satisfying them."

"Do you ever act Lyly's plays?"

"No, he writes for the private theatres, and, besides, his language is a trifle too fancy for the kind of audience we have."

Will was sorry to hear that, for he had been captivated by Lyly's works, which he had borrowed from Richard. He had become enchanted with the fancy words and the sprightly tone and the way the man could turn and twist his sentences. It was a kind of foolery, he thought, this euphuism.

For the next three months Will worked as a copyist for Wilson. A few times he hesitantly suggested changes in the writing, all the while amazed at his own boldness in doing so. At first Wilson was not sure that he liked the ideas Shakespeare offered, but he soon began to accept them, and even expressed his admiration for them.

"You seem to have a slight turn for this sort of thing, Will," he said. "That was a pretty little song you wrote for the fourth act. We'll use it. And that neat play on words and the punning you put into the Lord Mayor's speech will stay in."

In what leisure time he had during the day Will explored all the odd and unusual corners of London. He had no money to waste in taverns or on puppet shows, but he found the people on the streets and the overheard conversations more interesting than anything money could have bought. He spent long hours along the Thames, where he met many sailors and coaxed them to talk about shipwrecks and storms, ports they had seen and the lonely, tempest-torn islands their ships had sailed past. Many of Will's evenings were spent with Richard Field and his wife. Old Vautrollier's library, a small room in the house, was as much an attraction for him as was their friendship.

He still lived in his attic room, suffering its dampness and lack of comfort amid wistful thoughts of his mother's fine, clean beds at home. Letters from his family assured him that they were all well and healthy; their livelihood was precarious but not desperate. After three months of steady work he was able to scrape together a pound and send it to Stratford by one of Richard's trusted friends.

Finally Will was given a small part. The play was a very poor comedy, and only Kempe's ability to make such wonderful clowning faces and Thomas Pope's superb acting, which triumphed over the worthlessness of his part, prevented the crowd from rioting onto the stage. As it was, the players could hardly make themselves heard over the periodic boos and catcalls.

"What can an actor do with such rubbish?" Pope complained to Will afterward. "You certainly did your best with the lines you had. Kempe said that you have natural talent and promise as a player, and I agree with him. By the way, that little song in the third act—they tell me you wrote that. It was the best thing in the entire play."

Will was deeply pleased, for such men as Pope did not praise lightly.

Another and better part for him in a better play soon came along and he worked very hard, practicing in his room alone at night and accepting the criticism and suggestions of his fellow players. On opening night he did well and the next night he did even better. After that second performance he thought that the other actors were beginning to treat him almost like one of themselves.

His salary was raised slightly, and it was time he had some extra money, for his clothes were wearing thin and he was as embarrassed by the patches in them as he was by their out-of-date style. He headed for a tailor's shop, but once there, any dreams of bottle-green velvet or canary-yellow silk vanished as soon as he heard the prices. "For that much money," he marveled, "you could buy a small cottage in Stratford."

The tailor was disgusted when Will chose an inexpensive, dark blue material, but when he learned that this young man was an actor, he became all smiles. "For you I will do my best. There is nothing I like so much as a good play."

So the inelegant material was at least cut and fitted to Will extremely well. The tight-fitting doublet came down below the waist and was stiffened over the chest with thin whalebone in fashionable imitation of the old coats of armor. The breeches were puffed slightly and caught tightly just above the knee. The neck of the doublet could be open to reveal white shirt or covered with ruff or collar. At his own expense, the tailor had added a fluting of lighter blue, stitched with silver thread, around the armholes, and over the shoulder. He also had another surprise: at the bottom of the short cape, which fastened at the back of the neck, he had added a narrow band of silvery fur. "You may owe me for it if you like," he said when Will protested.

Now he could walk the streets of London without feeling ashamed of his appearance.

Thomas Pope nodded in approval when he saw Will. "Good clothes are important. A man must dress well here or be ignored. Not only companies but sometimes an individual can catch the eye of a nobleman and then his fortune is made. Since plays and acting are so popular, these nobles like to claim acquaintance with some of us. I think, young Shakespeare," Pope added slyly, his eyes twinkling, "that we must show you off. We have no performance today and no rehearsal. There's a play opening this afternoon at Henslowe's Rose Theatre. If it is no good at least I may be able to introduce you to someone of importance."

It was Will's first visit to a real theatre. The Rose was not very different in design from the courtyard of an inn, except that the balconies were there solely for people to sit in. The seats were permanent, as was the stage. The Rose had one thing

63

that was new to him—a room at the back, over the exits and entrances to the stage.

"You'll see why," Pope said as they took their seats. "If a scene is supposed to take place inside a house, they play it up there. And the floor has a trap door to let down spirits from heaven or ghosts or anything like that."

From the moment the prologue was spoken and the actors stepped out to perform *Tamburlaine*, Will knew that he was seeing something the like of which he had never imagined. He sat, motionless, his hands gripping the railing of the balcony, enthralled by what was taking place down on the stage.

Nothing had prepared him for this. The plays he had seen in Stratford, the ones he had acted in on the road and in London, the ones Wilson wrote—all of them were silly, jiggery-pokery things compared to this. Beside him, Pope was spellbound too, only once in a while heaving a great sigh of astonishment or crying out in pleasure at a particularly moving speech.

When the play ended the whole audience filed out in stunned silence. Will himself did not move until Pope touched his arm, and only then did he get up, still under the spell of the drama he had just seen, and follow his companion out of the theatre. Slowly he returned to reality.

"Who wrote this *Tamburlaine*?" were his first words to Pope.

"A young man just down from Cambridge University, Christopher Marlowe. It is said that he is a dangerous fellow, full of treasonable ideas, against both church and state. I say, whatever his politics, he writes as no other playwright ever has."

They headed for THE MERMAID TAVERN, walking slowly and speaking of what they had seen. When they arrived, a large number of people were already seated at one table; it was an excited, laughing, gaily talking group.

When the two actors had settled themselves at a small table in one corner, Will shook his head as if to wake himself from a dream. "I never thought to see anything such as *Tamburlaine*. They say miracles are past, but was this not some sort of miracle?"

64

Pope nodded soberly. "I am a comedian and there was no comedy in the play, but of its magnificence there can be no question. It will put every playwright on his toes——"

Just then a roar of laughter from the large table interrupted them, and Pope half rose in his chair to see who was laughing. When he sat down again he leaned forward and spoke in a low tone:

"The man at the head of that table—the handsome, elegant man—is Sir Walter Raleigh, the Queen's favorite. Some years ago for his bravery in battle she knighted him, gave him Durham House and a large income from wine monopolies. But his fortunes go up and down. He's not in good favor since his colonies in the New World proved to be expensive failures. That's his favorite table, where he holds court, mingling with all kinds of people, educated and brilliant men of science and literature. Next to him on the left is Sir Francis Walsingham, another patron of the arts. I want you to meet him."

Walsingham had turned and so had a younger man beside him. What held Will's attention was the young man's face, with its wild, dark eyes burning with excitement. He would have been handsome but for a scar made by a dueling blade.

"Who is that one?" he asked.

Pope looked. "That's Christopher Marlowe, our illustrious playwright." He shook his head. "Drunk as usual."

Marlowe, who had been downing one glass of wine after another, was talking and laughing loudly.

"And next to him is the writer Robert Greene—a good writer but he lives with the scum of London. He's married to a girl whose brother is the best-known thief in town. Across from him is the Earl of Oxford; beside him is Thomas Kyd, the author of *The Spanish Tragedy*——"

There was a disturbance at the door as it opened and Edward Alleyn came in. The innkeeper of THE MERMAID saw him and shouted, "Alleyn! What ho, Tamburlaine!" Richard Tarleton was with Alleyn, but when he saw Will and Pope, he came over to their table while the black-bearded actor joined Raleigh's group.

65

"Ned, you were a prince of actors! You were everything I hoped my Tamburlaine would be." Marlowe spoke so loudly that he could be heard all through the room. Conversation at other tables ceased—everyone was listening.

Dignified, Alleyn inclined his head and said courteously, "With such a role, the worst of actors could not but do well."

"Then perhaps you will put in a word for me with Henslowe so he will part with another pound or two? I sold it to him for five pounds, but 'tis not enough. Must we writers starve while managers like Philip Henslowe get rich off us?"

Alleyn's face became angry. "Henslowe is my wife's father. I'll not hear him disparaged."

Thomas Kyd laid a hand on his arm. "Do not quarrel with Kit; he has drunk too much. Besides, there is truth in what he says."

Raleigh spoke then, in a tone too low to be heard, diverting their attention to end the unpleasant incident.

"Shall we take Will over and let him meet such company?" Pope asked Tarleton.

Will raised a quick hand in protest. "I would rather not, if it does not displease you."

"He is quite right," Tarleton said. "They are clever men and some are rich enough to be patrons. But it is a spendthrift and reckless company, and Will cannot afford to live as they do. He has a family and no money. I would not put such temptation in your way, Will. It is all too easy to fall into the habit of spending your time in taverns in such company."

Will did not contradict Tarleton, but his own reasons were quite different. With all his heart he longed to be one of that gay company, but pride kept him from it. Who was he? Why should such men be interested in a man who had accomplished nothing, who had neither high birth nor a high station in life to recommend him? What would they have said if he had been introduced? "A new player? Shows promise? Most interesting, Master Pope"—and then they would have turned back to each other and forgotten him. Kit Marlowe looked to be the same age as himself, and Will could not have borne either contempt or indifference from the man who had written *Tamburlaine.*

Just as he and Pope and Tarleton were leaving, a very young and slender man—still more boy than man—entered and, with an air of bravado, sauntered over to the big table to speak to the Earl of Oxford.

Pope nodded in his direction. "I think that is the young Earl of Southampton." Then he followed Tarleton out.

Will lingered for a moment. Something in the youth's face, something wistful, something proud, something hesitant about him as he spoke to Oxford, told Will the young nobleman, like himself, wanted to be part of that company and was not yet really accepted. Will felt a strange kinship with him, in spite of his own poverty and lack of achievement.

He walked home very slowly. He had caught a glimpse of glory that afternoon; he had seen what could be done on a stage. It was as if a curtain had been lifted from his own blindness. Now he knew what his true ambitions were. He had come to love the stage and acting . . . but how infinitely greater it would be to *write* for the theatre!

He realized that the desire to write had been growing steadily in him since he was a boy and had dreamed his dreams near the brooding castle of Kenilworth and in the mysterious Forest of Arden, since the time he had been the fireside storyteller in Richard Hathaway's cottage. Yet, until today, he had not been really aware of his deep need to create beautiful songs, poems, stories. *Tamburlaine* had been a revelation, an inspiration. Perhaps he, too, could write plays like that.

Will came home to his mean lodgings to find a note from Richard Field:

> If it interests you, Will, there is a splendid opening for a clerk in the Middle Temple law court. Come to me tomorrow at three, at St. Paul's, if convenient.

With a quick and final gesture he crumpled the note in his hand. What was the law to him now? Tonight he would start writing his first play!

Will sat down at the table and drew the candle nearer. For two hours he scribbled away and at the end of that time he tore the papers into little pieces.

It was not that writing came slow and hard for him. On the contrary, the words poured themselves out. But they were not the words he wanted. He found himself at times imitating Marlowe, at times Lyly; or else he was adopting the classical style of the Greeks and the Romans. But just as he felt he had written a speech that was good, he would see in it a poor imitation of Robert Wilson. Suddenly plots were all jumbled up in his head —every plot of every story he had ever heard or imagined.

He would not give up, however, because occasionally he wrote a speech or a whole page or just a few lines that satisfied him. From the very beginning he was writing better than Wilson, better than most of the writers of plays in London, but not yet as well as Marlowe. He became discouraged during the long nights when he went without sleep, when the quill pen cramped in his fingers and his body ached with fatigue, when for every ten words that sparkled or sang or soared there were a hundred that were lifeless, commonplace, dull. Then he would tear them up and remind himself that *Tamburlaine* had not been Marlowe's first play.

As a Cambridge student, Marlowe had studied composition, had written essays, plays, poetry. With no such training, with no assistance from teachers, or anyone else, William Shakespeare was teaching himself how to construct a plot, how to create characters, how to convey the action of a story or a man's thoughts and emotions—all in verse.

Unfortunately for his writing—but fortunately for his pocketbook—he became more and more in demand as an actor. The Earl of Leicester died and his company came under the patronage of Lord Strange, with Edward Alleyn as manager. Will worked for him, steadily getting bigger, better parts. One week, when there was no role to fit Will, he still had no rest because Tarleton begged him to accept a part in a new production that the Queen's Men were putting on in Burbage's Theatre. Here Will met the older Burbage and the young Richard again.

Richard remembered well their meeting as young boys and the two became instant friends. Richard had grown into a slim, dark, romantic-looking man; but underneath this handsome exterior was an ambition and a growing talent that would take him far. The new friendship was good for both young men, who found that they could talk to each other as they could to no one else.

"Why do you want so much to write plays?" Richard asked Will one day. "Is anything better than being the finest actor in London? That's what I will be someday, as good as or better than Alleyn. Why must you work all day and then sit up all night writing?"

Will shrugged his shoulders. "Why? He must needs go that the devil drives, Richard. You know that. Something inside consumes me with flames; I cannot rest. A power I have—but of what strength and nature, I don't know. I only know that I *must* write. Sometimes I think I have done well, then I look at the words the next day and, 'Fool, fool,' I say! Such poor, barren, means attempts . . . Yet I cannot stop. Sometimes I do please myself though. What do you think of this?" he asked shyly:

> Crabbed age and youth cannot live together:
> Youth is full of pleasance, age is full of care;
> Youth like summer morn, age like winter weather;
> Youth is full of sport, age's breath is short;
>   Youth is nimble, age is lame;
> Youth is hot and bold, age is weak and cold;
>   Youth is wild, and age is tame . . .

Richard's dark eyes widened. "But that is excellent, Will! I withdraw my criticism. You have a gift far greater than I had dreamed of."

"I shall do much better than that, I *know* I shall," Will promised fervently.

8

It was now 1588, and Shakespeare went on tour with the Queen's Men because they offered him more of a share in the earnings and all his expenses paid. But Tarleton had died and without him the troupe was not as popular, which meant that Will and Richard Burbage and Cuthbert, Richard's younger brother, and the rest of the actors had to work twice as hard, play in every village and town they possibly could, to try to make, in many performances, the shillings that Tarleton could have brought in one afternoon.

The troupe came back to London to find tremendous events taking place. As the players rode into the City, they had difficulty moving through the crowds of people going in the other direction, some on foot or on horseback, others in carts. Some of the folk were running pellmell.

Will called out to one of the passers-by, "Where are you going? What has happened?"

"The Spaniards are coming! Run for your lives!" the man yelled without pausing.

Reaching the heart of the City, the actors found that it was true: the Spaniards had at last made good their threat. Their Armada was too huge, their ships too powerful, to be contained forever inside harbors by Drake's smaller vessels. The Spanish fleet had broken out and set sail for England, with terror preceding it as fantastic rumors spread about the size and the invincibility of the ships and about the cruelty of the Spaniards.

In actuality, only a few fled from London, while the vast majority of Englishmen stayed sturdy and strong, refusing to be intimidated. The Spanish threat welded all classes, all kinds of men and women, into one nation.

For days the City seethed and rocked as men armed themselves with swords grown rusty with age; with crossbows they had not touched for years. Wild stories spread of "eyewitness" accounts of the Spaniards landing on the coast. Then came the news. It was an English victory! In the middle of July, Elizabeth's naval commanders, with their small ships, had so harried and harassed and fired the huge unwieldy ships that those not sunk had slunk away in defeat. There had been no invasions of the coast of England.

London went wild with pride and success. They adored their Queen, they toasted Drake and Hawkins, Nottingham and Frobisher. Britannia ruled the seas and it was a glorious day throughout the land.

Will Shakespeare joined the noisy, triumphant men and women thronging the streets, as proud and as drunk with patriotism as they were. Will heard them say "we English," and realized that this was a new and wonderful thing. Formerly it had been a man from Kent or Devonshire or York; now the people felt united, one, *English.*

Perhaps this was something to write about . . . Why not? He had learned the history of his country from Holinshed's *Chronicles of England, Scotland and Ireland,* but few other men knew more than little bits and pieces that were part legend, part fact. The idea excited him and, wanting to consider it further, he wandered down to the Thames where he could escape from the crowds. He leaned against a stone wall and watched the tiny lights from thousands of burning torches bobbing up and down in the boats.

His imagination was stirring as it had not been in years. Why write about oriental monarchs or go back to the Greeks for inspiration when right under his nose was the best source of all for plays—England's history, filled with the drama of kings

71

crowned and kings dethroned, of conspiracies and murder, of battles lost and won, of valorous deeds and sinister intrigues.

Yes, he would do it. He would write plays about these things— and he would not tear them up. So excited was he that he turned his back on the river and hastened through the mobbed streets to his dreary lodgings. But this time he did not notice the depressing front door, the cobwebby stairs, the stale odors. He closed the door of his tiny room and he sat down to reread Holinshed's *Chronicles*. Losing all sense of time, he read far into the night, until the candle stub flickered and failed and he was forced to put the book down.

In the days and months that followed, he studied the history of England when he was not busy acting. Out of all the centuries, what fascinated him most was the time from 1455 to 1485, the years of the War of the Roses. This was not surprising for he had spent his boyhood near Kenilworth, where the Earl of Warwick, the Kingmaker, had once lived. A hundred years before, Warwick had been one of the greatest nobles in England and had played a prominent part in the War of the Roses—a part that was known by every lad in Stratford ever since.

In 1422 King Henry V died and his very young son was crowned Henry VI. Quarrels broke out between the Duke of York and the Duke of Somerset. They were bitter rivals, and one day, in the Temple Garden, they almost came to blows over a trivial legal matter. The Duke of York plucked a white rose from a bush and asked all who stood by him to do the same; the Duke of Somerset plucked a red rose. Then, one by one, the nobles lined up choosing white or red roses, and the division was made that would lead to civil war. The Earl of Warwick chose white, for York, scheming to push York's claim to the throne. It was a good claim, through his great-grandfather; as good a claim as that of Henry VI. Henry had inherited through a Lancaster ancestor, so the War of the Roses was to become also a war between York and Lancaster.

In the meantime France was trying to recover French soil which had been conquered by Henry V, the young King's dead father. Joan of Arc had come to the rescue of the French Dauphin and was leading his armies. This war went on so long that the Pope finally interceded and demanded that England and France make an honorable peace. Joan of Arc was to be burned at the stake as a witch; King Henry must marry a French princess to bind the two nations. The princess, Margaret of Anjou whom Henry married, was a disappointment to many English nobles and they resented her. She was not of first rank; she brought no rich dowry to England—in fact, Henry had promised to give the duchies of Anjou and Maine to her father. Henry loved his bride but York and the other nobles were furious.

The Lancaster party of the red rose rallied around the Queen; those of the white rose around the Duke of York, especially when they saw that Queen Margaret was determined to get control over her weak, gentle husband and rule England herself. While Warwick stayed in England and roused support for the Duke of York, he himself went to Ireland to put down a rebellion there. When his job was done, York rode back to London at the head of an army powerful enough for him to insist to the King that he be named as heir to the throne instead of any of Henry's sons.

The King might have agreed because he was weak but Queen Margaret and the nobles of the red rose resisted. There was a great battle at St. Albans; York was victorious; the King and Queen fled; Warwick urged the Duke of York to reach the city before the King could summon Parliament to argue the matter.

When Henry and Margaret reached London, York was already seated on the throne in the House of Parliament. Meekly Henry agreed to disinherit his own son if he were allowed to continue to be Henry VI during his own lifetime.

Queen Margaret did not agree. She gathered around her all the Lancaster red rose faction and with them a huge army and advanced to meet York near Wakefield. York's youngest son, the Earl of Rutland, was brutally killed. York was captured and the Queen mocked him, showing him his son's bloody clothes. She put a paper crown on York's head, taunting him with his ambitions, then his head was cut off and set up on the spikes over the gates of the castle of York.

Warwick joined Edward and Richard, York's sons, and there was a battle near Towton in which Margaret and Henry were finally defeated. Henry was imprisoned in the Tower and York's oldest son, Edward, was crowned Edward IV of England.

Although this did not end the turbulent history of the family of the Duke of York, it did put an end to the War of the Roses.

It was this period in England's history that fascinated Will. His imagination was filled with knights and lords in armor; with a spineless King and a cruel yet proud Queen. He felt their emotions and understood their ambitions, their hatreds and loves, their jealousies and honors. The words each would say to the other spun themselves out in his mind even while he was acting, rehearsing, prompting, taking every possible job in the theatre to earn more money for his family.

The Queen's Men were rapidly going downhill. Ned Alleyn, of the Lord Strange Company, was the favorite actor of all London. He had moved the company to Henslowe's theatre, but Will played there reluctantly because he did not like Henslowe's business tactics.

So in the summer of 1589, when the Earl of Pembroke's Men went on tour, Will went with them gladly. He was pleased to find that he had more time to himself than he had had since he had begun to act. Since all the plays had been rehearsed in London, he had nothing to do but act his roles each afternoon. The rest of the day was his to do with as he pleased. For over a week he spent his leisure time wandering in meadows and forests, swimming in small streams or sitting idly in the sun. His mind and body had been constantly under the pressure of work, and now he relaxed.

Thinking of the plays he wanted to write, he saw at least one reason why he had torn up most of them. He had been imitating Marlowe's weaknesses as well as his strengths. The speeches of Kit's characters rang like trumpets—but they never stopped blowing. Tamburlaine made love in the same violent tone in which he talked war; he addressed servants using the same high-sounding, five-syllable words he used in speaking to kings. All of the characters sounded alike; they were gigantic figures but not human beings.

Would a weak, cowardly Henry VI use the same kind of words as did a valiant Warwick? Would Queen Margaret and the wife of Gloucester sound the same?

He went to bed one night with such thoughts spinning in his head and he woke the next morning knowing *exactly* how he would tell the story of the War of the Roses. Without thinking of breakfast he dressed hurriedly, went to the head of the stairs and called down to the courtyard for the serving man to bring him a table to work on and quill pens and paper. Thinking that all actors were mad anyway, the servant grumbled only a little at the extra work and the early hour and brought everything he had been asked to fetch.

Will heard nothing—not the grumbling, not the horses whinnying in the inn stable, not the faint sounds of the tapster boy getting water from the well. His total concentration was focused on the words that his pen was rapidly tracing across the paper:

Act 1. Scene 1. London, Westminster Abbey
Flourish of trumpets

After the trumpets would come the Dead March for the funeral of old King Henry V, the great monarch who had conquered so much of France for England. Then the Duke of Bedford would speak, in sorrow for that death, and then the Duke of Gloucester, uncle to the infant King and his protector, would add his words of praise for the dead Henry V:

> England ne'er had a king until his time.
> Virtue he had, deserving to command;
> His brandish'd sword did blind men with his beams . . .

Even at the funeral the quarrels would begin. Soon a messenger would enter with word that France was in arms against England.

Will was creating the background for the troubles to come.

He was writing well. He knew it and it gave him deep, quiet satisfaction. He forgot about food, the place, the hour, until the hullaballoo down in the courtyard brought him to a halt, realizing that the audience was arriving for the afternoon performance. Reluctantly he put down his pen.

Immediately after the show the players were on their horses and riding off to the next town. The next morning Will woke early and again began writing. The scene now switched to France, and he wrote more slowly and carefully because he must introduce Joan of Arc. Like all the Englishmen of his time, Will believed she had been a witch; nevertheless, he knew that she was a brave and splendid woman, more courageous than her Dauphin.

He pictured her as she was to the French: a peasant girl chosen by God to lead Frenchmen to victory. Skillfully, he showed her as she appeared to the English: a devil, a woman of no morals or scruples, a fiend. Yet to both she was a symbol of courage.

Soon afterward Will wrote, in one night and morning, the famous scene in the Temple Garden between the Duke of York and the Earl of Somerset. He drew a skillful, dramatic portrait of York that was to make him a favorite character with audiences. The fiercely proud, ambitious duke had captured Will's imagination, and from the moment Richard plucked a white rose and held it up as the symbol of the House of York, he began to dominate every scene in which he appeared:

> And, by my soul, this pale and angry rose,
> As cognizance of my blood-drinking hate,
> Will I for ever, and my faction, wear;
> Until it wither with me to my grave,
> Or flourish to the height of my degree.

Somerset accepted the challenge with a red rose:

> . . . Thou shalt find us ready for thee still;
> And know us, by these colours, for thy foes;
> For these my friends, in spite of thee, shall wear.

Will scarcely knew or cared where they rode or in what town they played. His eyes saw not the England of his own day but the England of Henry VI. He chose to write in prose and blank verse instead of poetry, because he felt that the story was too serious to be told in rhyming speeches and he was afraid that the play would develop a jingling rhythm that would spoil the intense drama.

The day before they reached London, Will finished the play, ending it with the burning of Joan of Arc, the intervention of the Pope for a peaceful settlement between France and England, and Henry's consent to marry Margaret of Anjou. The closing words were spoken by the Earl of Suffolk, another power-seeking noble who was responsible for bringing the Frenchwoman to England:

> Margaret shall now be queen, and rule the king;
> But I will rule both her, the king and realm.

Shakespeare put down the pen, got up, stretched and went to the window to gaze at the rolling green countryside. Tomorrow they would be back in London, where acting companies and theatres competed with one another. The newly written play still held him in its grip; he repeated the last two lines to himself and liked them. Suffolk was not as important as York but his words made an effective ending because it contained a promise of further struggle and intrigue. If this play was successful, another one would have to be written to carry on the story of Henry VI and the War of the Roses.

If . . . Suddenly, as he stood at the window, he felt completely exhausted, drained of all strength. With this fatigue came doubts. Was it a *good* play? He had read parts of it to other members of Pembroke's company and they had marveled at it, saying that it was wonderful. But did they know? Perhaps they were trying to be agreeable, or were so anxious to have a new play to present in London that they had merely said it was good.

Like a man benumbed—fearful one moment and hopeful the

77

next—Will rode in with the troupe to London, moved to cleaner lodgings and reported the next day at THE BELLE SAUVAGE.

"We're buying your *Henry VI*," the manager of Pembroke's Men told him. "We'll use it as our first production in London this year, to attract attention. Audiences are crying for new plays, and this one of yours is excellent.

Will heard the compliment but it meant nothing to him. He went through the rehearsals like a sleepwalker, rousing himself only when he had to make a change now and then in an actor's lines. He was surprised, as was the whole company, at how few revisions were necessary. His experience in the theatre had been good for him, training his eye and ear to the needs of the stage. He seemed to know instinctively how long a scene should be to hold the attention of an audience, how much an actor could say in one speech without losing the force of passion or anger, how to build up emotions from climax to climax.

The opening day of the performance of *Henry VI* finally came. The inn courtyard was crowded with a full audience. During the first part of the play Will thought only of himself as a player, since he had a minor role and appeared only in the first scenes. But when his part was done and he stepped off the stage, behind a curtain where he could watch the audience, he was not Shakespeare the actor but Shakespeare the playwright, and he suffered tortures that he had never thought possible.

Why was the audience so silent when old, wise Gloucester snarled back at the lords who tried so hard to rob him of his power over the young king? Were the people in the balconies actually leaning forward breathlessly to catch every word that York said as he recounted his birthright, proving that his succession to the throne was as justified as Henry's? The audience who stood on the ground had stopped chewing nuts and gulping ale . . . Could that mean they were really interested?

Then, in the middle of Act III, Scene ii, when the English and French forces fought for the city of Rouen and Talbot, the brave English commander, said:

And I,—as sure as English Henry lives,
And as his father here was conqueror;
As sure as in this late-betrayed town
Great Coeur-de-lion's heart was buried:
So sure I swear, to get the town or die

the old courtyard was swept with hoarse cheering from the audience, balcony and yard alike. The action onstage had to stop while the cheers and the thumping of feet went on and on and cries of "Talbot!" "England!" were shouted from all sides.

William Shakespeare remained tense and stiff. Was this merely patriotism? But by the play's end there could no longer be any doubt. THE BELLE SAUVAGE was aswirl with a shouting, applauding crowd. Will had been an actor too long not to know when an audience thoroughly loved a play. *Henry VI* had taken the people by storm and they cheered the actors, the courageous Talbot, England. The one name they did not cheer was "Shakespeare" for he was as yet unknown. But it was *his* play they were cheering. He felt a glorious happiness that was unlike anything he had ever known before.

The other actors were lavish with their praise. "All the time I was onstage," the actor who played York told him enthusiastically, "I could feel the crowd responding to everything I said, everything I did. I'm not Ned Alleyn—I don't ordinarily pull a crowd with me, no matter what the words are. It was your story and your words that did it, Will."

He was paid four pounds for *Henry VI.* He went out of THE BELLE SAUVAGE with the money in his pocket, walking on air. He thought London was beautiful and its people kind and wonderful. He saw none of the dirt or the squalor or smelled the stench of the open sewers. At that moment he was proud to be Will Shakespeare. He was supremely happy.

9

Henry VI continued to attract more and more people to the inn courtyard. The crowning moment came when Pembroke's Men were commanded to appear in the Middle Temple and perform the play before the young lawyers and the gentlemen who amused themselves by studying at the Temple. For the first time Will saw the richly paneled hall with its raised dais at one end and the musicians' gallery, fronted with its carved wooden screen, at the other. Had he taken Richard Field's advice, he told himself, he might have come here to be a clerk and perhaps one day a lawyer. More likely he would have remained just a clerk, he thought in wry amusement.

The gentlemen liked *Henry* VI as well as the public audience had. Will, listening inconspicuously to their comments, learned that it was his ability to make real people out of historical figures that caught their interest.

With such encouragement he immediately began a second play, Part Two of *Henry* VI, picking up the story where he had left off. The English nobles who wore the white rose of York were furious at the marriage of arrogant Margaret of Anjou to Henry, while those of the red rose rallied around the queen. The play ended after the battle of St. Albans, with York victorious and Warwick urging him to hurry to London to establish himself and his rights before Parliament. This was as much as he could tell in one play; the rest of the historic War of the Roses would have to wait for a sequel.

The first part of *Henry* VI had been so well liked that the announcement of Part Two drew even larger crowds, who applauded this play as much as they had the first. It was a proud moment for Will when he wrote to Anne that two of his dramas were being acted out on the London stage and he could send her five pounds.

True, Shakespeare's plays had not created the sensation in London that *Tamburlaine* had. Marlowe had been a bold pioneer and had done something so different that his name and his play had been on everyone's lips, making him famous overnight. Will knew that the London public liked his plays and that the gentlemen-lawyers of the Temple had been most complimentary, but what did the other writers think of him?

One late autumn day he and Richard Burbage met in the garden of THE MERMAID TAVERN.

"It's true then that you plan to join the Lord Strange's Men, Will?" Richard asked.

Shakespeare nodded. "I don't care much for Henslowe, but the Earl of Pemberton does not seem to be able to establish his company in London. Henslowe, owning the Rose Theatre, does not have to share the profits with an innkeeper. Pemberton's group must go on tour again and they have sold both my plays to Henslowe—so, little as I like it, I must work for Lord Strange."

"I fear that I must too, sooner or later," Richard said ruefully. "The Queen's Men are having a hard time scraping up money to buy new plays. My father thought it a fine thing when the Queen gave us her name and protection, but Her Majesty is notoriously stingy with money. How I wish we could have bought your last *Henry VI*! It was beautifully written, Will, but the actor who played York did not do justice to the part, as I could have." Richard was not being immodest. He was very serious about his work and knew his own talents.

"When you say it was beautifully written, are you speaking as my friend or as a critic?" Will asked, smiling.

"As a critic. Oh, Will, what would I not give to have played York!" He broke into a passionate delivery of one of the speeches, and as he finished, there was a burst of applause from a window of the tavern. Richard and Will turned abruptly to see Sir Walter Raleigh and a half-dozen other men clapping and beckoning to them. Without thinking, Richard had raised his voice as he spoke the lines, and their challenge had gone ringing out across the garden.

"I regret, Sir Walter," said Richard as he and Will came to the window, "if we have disturbed you."

"You call that a disturbance? It was fine entertainment and I think I know the lines from having seen the play at THE BELLE SAUVAGE. An excellent work! I thought Kit Marlowe here had written it but he denies the authorship."

"May I then present the rightful author? William Shakespeare, my lord."

Will bowed, feeling a deep flush rise to his cheeks. He was embarrassed less by the kindly look that Sir Walter gave him than by the stares of three other men: Christopher Marlowe, the portly, sedate Michael Drayton, and the pasty-faced, unsmiling Robert Greene. He knew them all by sight and reputation, but had not met all of them before. Known as the "university wits," along with Thomas Kyd, John Lyly and others, they had written the plays that had set the fashion in London. What would such men think of him?

Marlowe reached drunkenly out of the window. "Your hand, Master Shakespeare! This work of yours, this Henry play, is a splendid thing and I am proud to be thought its author. Come in, come in. Join us . . ."

But when Will and Richard stepped over the low windows and took seats at the long table, they found that Marlowe's good opinion was not shared by Robert Greene, a sour man whose talents were fast being ruined by his corrupt ways. He stared with sullen eyes at Will across the table. "I have heard of you." The tone if not the words were offensive. "You're an actor; I think you were a stagehand too. Is that where you learned to write? Keeping your ears open so that you could copy other men's plays?"

Will was no swaggering brawler but his temper could be quick. Before Greene had finished speaking, he had pushed back his stool and was halfway to his feet, his hand on his sword. "Sir, you——"

Richard's hand on his arm pulled him down. Michael Drayton interrupted him before he could say another word. "Pay no attention to Greene. Sit down, please. And you, Robert, apologize. If there be a trifle of imitation in your plays, Master Shakespeare, it is a fault that all of us are guilty of. And there is much, much more in *Henry VI* that is original, and marvelously well said. You have learning and wit, sir, and if Greene does not apologize, I can only suspect him of jealousy."

"I? Jealous? Drayton, take care how you speak. I've slashed a man for less than that . . ."

The stratagem had succeeded and Greene's anger was now turned on Drayton, whose stolid good temper was bothered not one whit by it. Marlowe grinned at Will and Sir Walter smiled before he turned to converse with Thomas Kyd, who was seated at his left. Will's temper slowly subsided. The argument that was going on between Drayton and Greene, the noise created by the others as they talked back and forth across the table, had nothing to do with him and he was free to look about. He realized with a start that he was at last sitting where he had once longed so desperately to be. He was actor and author; he was accepted, complimented; he had even stirred one man to a jealous outburst. But he did not feel the pleasure he had expected.

Somehow the stature of these men had diminished. Sir Walter was worried, uncertain of his place at court and more and more frequently out of favor with Elizabeth. Marlowe, still drinking too much, had become careless about his dress and speech. Thomas Kyd, Kit's close friend, watched anxiously as Marlowe called loudly for more wine. Walsingham, who sat next to Marlowe, was a man of clouded reputation: he was said to be involved in all kinds of intrigue to further his own political ambitions and had dragged the playwright into it.

No, Will was not impressed by any of them. He was glad that he was not really one of them. The years had given him better judgment and it was Richard Burbage—his earnest, hard-working friend—whom he valued above these others. His eye traveled further down the table and he saw with surprise that one man was looking at him steadily. It was Henry Wriothesley, the Earl of Southampton, two years older, more handsome, more assured of himself, than the first time Will had seen him. Yet he had a boyish, clean quality that set him apart from the rest.

It flashed through Will's mind that both he and the Earl were now well received here, yet neither of them fitted in.

When he saw Will looking at him, Southampton spoke: "Master Shakespeare, I am curious about a certain thing. You are actor as well as author. Do you not find that these two professions are at odds with each other?" Immediately the whole table fell silent to listen. "Kit tells us that he is always quarreling with the actors in his plays because they want to make changes that would ruin some of his best speeches."

It was Burbage who answered for Will. "No, it is the opposite, my Lord. Will is an actor and thinks as an actor. He provides exits and entrances for us. He knows, as an actor, that if one speech has taken all a man's energy to deliver, then he must let his voice rest. If he has another big scene immediately, the actor will not do justice to it. Why, I have had, in one ridiculous play, to fight a duel and then be expected to play a love scene. I was panting and gasping for breath when I was supposed to be murmuring soft, sweet, gentle words of love."

Southampton was persistent. "But, Master Shakespeare, if the stage is foremost in your mind, does it not worry you that your plays will be as artificial, as unlike our real mortal selves, as is the theatre?"

Will thought for a moment, then said, "Sir, all the world's a stage. And all the men and women merely players: they have their exits and their entrances; and one man in his time plays many parts."

"How is this so?"

"His acts being seven ages," Will explained. "At first, the infant, mewling and puking in the nurse's arms. And then, the whining school-boy, with his satchel, and shining morning face, creeping like snail unwillingly to school. And then, the lover, sighing like furnace, with a woeful ballad made to his mistress' eyebrow. Then a soldier, full of strange oaths, and bearded like the pard, jealous in honor, sudden and quick in quarrel, seeking the bubble reputation even in the cannon's mouth. And then the justice, in fair round belly, with good capon lined, with eyes severe and beard of formal cut, full of wise saws and modern instances: and so he plays his part. The sixth age shifts into the lean and slipper'd pantaloon, with spectacles on nose and pouch on side, his youthful hose, well saued, a world too wide for his shrunk shank; and his big manly voice, turning again toward childish treble, pipes and whistles in his sound." Will was smiling at his own imagery. "Last scene of all, that ends this strange eventful history, is second childishness, and mere oblivion, sans teeth, sans eyes, sans taste, sans everything."

"Oh, well said! Well said, Will Shakespeare!" Kit Marlowe was so excited that he pounded his tankard on the table.

Raleigh nodded and in his eyes was a new respect. "A pretty conceit, a good turn of phrase."

To these men brilliance of conversation meant everything. The young Earl of Southampton was looking at him in frank astonishment. "I own it, if you will accept my speaking plain, that I did not expect such wit from a player. I would like to know you better, Will Shakespeare."

Will rose, bowed to Southampton, thanked them all courteously for their company and signaled to Burbage. The others protested but he insisted that they must leave. When he and Richard were out on the street, the latter said, "I like not such company."

"Nor I," Will agreed.

Now he saw how fortunate he had been to have had to work so hard these past years without money to spend in taverns every night. He was young; he loved good company, good talk and laughter; he had pride and a need to be admired. But suppose by some chance he had been drawn into this group from the beginning? Might he not have become like Greene and Marlowe? They were wasting their talents on empty pleasures.

As he started home, Will was already thinking about his next play. Even though the longed-for moment in the tavern had been a disappointment, it had given him new courage and boldness for future play-writing.

He wanted to go on with the story of the War of the Roses and finish the third part of *Henry VI*. He also was considering a comedy, for Kempe had sought him out and asked him to try his hand at it. Will was curious to see if he could. There was a play by Plautus about twin sons that he had always liked, and he thought he could make certain changes and adapt it for the London stage. He even had a title for it—*The Comedy of Errors*.

Before he went to sleep that night he remembered the handsome Earl of Southampton, and a daring thought came to him. Could he risk it . . . hope for it? Could he possibly interest Southampton in becoming his patron?

If a writer, an artist, a poet, was to have any chance for fame and fortune, it was necessary for him to obtain the support and backing of a great lord. Walsingham was Marlowe's patron, other writers were sponsored by other members of the nobility. But he was William Shakespeare, the son of a glove-maker, an actor who had not been too proud to do anything useful behind stage as well as out in front. He decided that he would have to wait until he had written something good enough that he could dedicate it to Southampton and hope to please him by so doing —instead of being frowned upon for such impertinence.

He drew the coarse blanket over his shoulders and tried in vain to fall asleep. Ambition had received a powerful spur and his mind raced from Southampton to his comedy and from it to the new plot of the last part of the *Henry VI* story. Which would he write next?

It was Philip Henslowe, however, who decided the issue for Will. Working for the Lord Strange Company was quite different from being a member of Pemberton's group. Will was no longer his own man, for Henslowe ruled his actors and writers with an iron hand. Robert Greene was his principal playwright and, for several months, it seemed as if Henslowe intended to keep Will so busy acting he would have no chance to write. Then one day he handed him a manuscript and demanded that he re-write it. When Will protested that he was already working on a play of his own, a comedy, Henslowe was not interested.

"I have all the comedies I need at this time—a good stock of them," he said precisely as if he were talking about merchandise he had bought from a store. "See what you can do with this."

This was an old Dutch play called *Aran en Titus*. Will tackled it savagely, disliking it, yet realizing how shrewd a man Henslowe was to choose on occasional story that would please the taste of the Londoners who gloried in bear-baiting, hangings and executions, and who liked nothing better than to run hooting after some poor wretch who was being whipped through the streets of London for her sins. Yes, this play, which Will retitled *Titus Andronicus*, would suit the capricious moods of the public that applauded the blood-and-gore horror stories one day and, the next, cheered the lightest, most fragile of poetic dramas.

Will did his best but his heart was not in it. His growing skill made even this tale of lunatic, bestial horror believable, but as he listened backstage, on the day of the performance, to the screams and cheers of the audience it brought back unpleasant memories of the Bear Garden, where he had witnessed the same response to brutality.

Henslowe was well pleased with *Titus* and asked for more like it, but Will refused.

It was now 1589 and one day Richard Burbage came to ask Will if he would write another play about Henry VI for the Queen's Men. "You have the right to sell it where you please," he pointed out. "Our company has managed to get enough money to pay you a few pounds and to put on this production. It would be a favor to us and a kindness to my father if you would do it."

Reluctantly Will agreed. It meant putting aside *The Comedy of Errors* once again, but Richard was his friend and he had great admiration for old James Burbage.

Will flung himself into the work on the last part of *Henry VI*, writing morning and night, when he was not acting, going without sleep, seeing no one.

He went through the next weeks like a man living a dreamlike eixstence. He grew thin and lost color in his face. His eyes ached from working long hours at night with only flickering candles to light his pages. But he was happy.

Now it was the Duke of York and his sons who dominated the story, along with the Earl of Warwick. Throughout the play there was a hint of trouble still to come. The third son, Richard the Crookback, now given the Duke of Gloucester's estates and titles, had already begun to plot how he could rid himself of all his brothers and snatch the crown of England for himself.

At last the play was finished and the Queen's Men began rehearsals. Will persuaded Henslowe that he was not well enough to act on the day *Henry VI*, Part Three, was to be performed, and he went to the theatre to see it.

Never before had he watched any of his plays from out front. He took his seat in the balcony, surprised to find himself more nervous than when he was backstage, waiting to go on. All around him people were cracking nuts, munching apples, drinking ale, and he wondered in despair how it was possible for such people to care what happened to the characters in his play.

These chattering, noisy Londoners hardly seemed *human*! The man on his right was an apprentice who was boasting of how many customers his master had coming to his silver shop, at the same time taking such great, enormous bites of bread and cold bacon that he barely got the words out. On Will's left was a giddy woman flirting with three fashionably dressed men on the bench behind her.

He had a sudden urge to get up and bash their heads together. What were they doing here? What could they possibly understand of York's tragic despair over his son's death, or the desperate struggle between white rose and red rose.

Suddenly an abrupt stillness fell over the theatre. Out on the stage walked the Earl of Warwick, the Duke of York, his sons Edward and Richard, along with other nobles. A sign on the pillar onstage stated that the scene was the Parliament House in London. The actors were in mailed armor, having just come from a victorious battle over the Lancastrian forces. Warwick spoke:

>——Victorious prince of York,
>Before I see thee seated in that throne
>Which now the house of Lancaster usurps,
>I vow by heaven, these eyes shall never close.
>This is the palace of the fearful king,
>And this the regal seat: possess it, York:
>For this is thine, and not King Henry's heirs.

Will noticed that the apprentice leaned forward, dropping his food to the floor. The flirting woman had smiled once again at the men behind her, but not one of them paid any attention. No one coughed. No one moved.

Old James Burbage, as York, still had a voice that could shake the rafters or drop to a sweet gentleness. Young Richard Burbage, playing York's son Richard, was no longer a handsome young man but a hunchback, deformed, crafty, sinister, but fearless. Cuthbert Burbage played the weak Henry VI, who appeared in Parliament first to plead timidly, finally to beg:

>My Lord of Warwick, hear me but one word;——
>Let me, for this my life-time, reign as king.

Will felt the entire audience stir in anger, as if to give vent to their feelings. They roared with shock and fury and Will shouted along with them when the captured York faced Margaret of Anjou on the battlefield:

>O tiger's heart, wrapp'd in a woman's hide!
>How coulds't thou drain the life-blood of the child,
>To bid the father wipe his eyes withal,
>And yet be seen to bear a woman's face?

The apprentice on Will's right shook his fist at Queen Margaret who was holding the bloody napkin she had dipped into the wounds of York's dead son, to flaunt it in the father's face before she killed him too. The woman on the other side was weeping.

Oh, thought Will, what a splendid fellow, that apprentice! What an intelligent, sensitive woman! Why, these Londoners obviously had a keen sense of appreciation and he loved every one of them. They caught the meaning of every line, they reacted to every character, they cheered when he hoped they would, cried when he wanted them to, and were breathlessly fascinated by crookback Richard, Duke of Gloucester.

Why? Will wondered. It was not just the superb acting of Richard Burbage. There was something more to it. Will had written far better than he had realized, making this deformed son of York such a subtle, clever character, so bold in his evil schemes, that he seemed to be more than just a man—he became a symbol of everything that was wicked and treacherous.

Will completely lost the rest of the play as he furiously searched for the clue to Richard's attraction. Being the personification of evil was not enough to make the audience so interested in him. Just as the play ended, with Yorkist Edward on the throne of England, Will suddenly decided that he knew what the answer was.

Gloucester was ruthless, selfish, determined to destroy everyone who got in his way—but he was also a victim. Without wanting to, the audience sympathized with the hunchback, who had been ridiculed and mocked from childhood, loved by no one —not even his family. Why, then, should he care for anyone? Thus Richard became terribly human in his sufferings, terribly strong in his thirsting for revenge, making him more than just a figure out of history.

The audience cheered wildly: The play was a triumph and Richard Burbage an overwhelming success. But Will did not linger at the theatre any longer than he had to. With the next play already fixed in his mind, he could hardly wait to get back to his room and begin work. He laid out three candles on the table for the long night ahead, quickly ate a frugal meal of bread and meat and cheese, then wrapped himself in his cloak and settled himself at the table.

10

At the top of the first page Will Shakespeare wrote the words: *Richard III.*

This was to be the story of the Duke of Gloucester's rise to the throne of England along a path strewn with betrayals, schemes, trickery and murder. One death after another of his brothers and nephews would lead him to the summit of power and glory.

The words came swiftly to his mind and swiftly his pen moved across the paper. The House of York was established, with Edward on the throne. His wife, Elizabeth, had already caused bad feelings by granting titles and land to her relatives. Richard made use of this to stir up trouble.

Will wrote steadily until twilight fell and he had to pause to light the first candle. He was oblivious to all the street noises outside his window. Nothing mattered but the play that was rapidly taking shape. He paused in his work to pace the floor. Gloucester's first speech was crucial, for it would have to present the full character of the man in order to make everything he did throughout the play believable and understandable. He went back to the table, read the opening words, wrote and crossed out and wrote again. At last he was satisfied with it:

> But I,—that am not shap'd for sportive tricks,
> Nor made to court an amorous looking-glass; . . .
> Cheated of feature by dissembling nature,
> Deform'd, unfinish'd, sent before my time
> Into this breathing world, scarce half made up,
> And that so lamely and unfashionable,

That dogs bark at me as I halt by them: . . .
I am determined to prove a villain,
And hate the idle pleasure of these days.
Plots have I laid, inductions dangerous, . . .
To set my brother Clarence, and the king,
In deadly hate, the one against the other.

By the time Will had finished the first two scenes all three candles had gutted themselves out and it was near four in the morning. Too tired to even undress, he threw himself on the bed, wrapped the cloak and blankets around him and slept deeply.

The next evening he wrote, and the next; on the fourth he had an engagement with the Fields. They were overjoyed to see him. "It has been weeks since we were last honored with your presence," Mistress Field exclaimed. "We thought you had forgotten us. We went to see your last play and, while I do not ordinarily like such things, I was greatly pleased with it. It was not in the least unseemly and much of it was poetical."

"Since you are determined to write, Will, why not write poetry?" Richard asked. "Acting companies seldom sell a play to print because others then steal it, but poems sell well and we print many of them. You could earn many more pounds that way than by selling a play to any company of actors."

This was something that Will had not considered before. "I do need the money," he admitted. "Letters from Stratford say that my father's affairs are slightly better, but my children are growing. Susanna and Hamnet and Judith need clothing and schooling." He smiled wryly. "Some say that ravens foster forlorn children, but mine have a father who must care for them. I long so much to see them," he added unhappily.

His daughter was now six and the twins were five. It was difficult for him to realize that the years had gone by so swiftly.

In May of 1590, Shakespeare completed *Richard III*, but the Queen's Men could not afford to buy it, being in so penniless a state that they were almost ready to dissolve the company. Will then went to see Edward Alleyn, who read the play and immediately declared that it was excellent and that he, and only he, would play Gloucester.

A superb cast was chosen, and money was not spared to provide handsome costumes and stage furnishings. On opening day, from the very first scene in the first act, no one onstage mattered but Gloucester. Alleyn, always a fine actor, now spoke lines that electrified the audience, and he was the first to portray one of Shakespeare's "great" characters.

The crowd that jammed the Rose Theatre was aroused to a pitch of almost intolerable emotion. They hated Gloucester: he maddened them, infuriated them—yet he captivated them. The people shouted in mounting fury as Gloucester committed one horrifying crime after another: the murder of the young Prince of Wales, the treacherous execution of Lord Hastings, the imprisonment of King Edward's two small sons after his death. And when the man whom Gloucester had hired to kill those two young boys, his nephews, spoke thus:

> The tyrannous and bloody act is done;
> The most arch deed of piteous massacre
> That ever yet this land was guilty of

the audience was in a frenzy of anger, screaming at the hunchbacked Ned Alleyn, who stood gloating on the stage.

When Gloucester became King, the other nobles, sickened by his foul deeds, rallied around Henry Tudor, forcing Richard to fight for his crown—and his life—at Bosworth Field. In that battle he was to lose both. But the night before the fray, he was visited in his dreams by the ghosts of all those whom he had slain or injured. Awakening from the nightmare, the tormented monarch brooded on his uncertain future:

> Have mercy, Jesu!—Soft; I did but dream—
> O, coward conscience, how dost thou afflict me! . . .
> My conscience hath a thousand several tongues,
> And every tongue brings me in a several tale;

And every tale condemns me for a villain . . .
I shall despair.—There is no creature loves me!
Nay, wherefore should they? Since that I myself
Find in myself no pity to myself.

In this study of the mind and heart of a man torn between guilt and defiance of the world that had made him guilty, between self-pity in one breath and scorn for himself in the next, Richard was a twisted figure of madness and greatness.

Hardly had the actors stepped forward on the stage to take their bows at the end of the play than the audience broke into wild, sustained cheering that seemed as if it would never stop. Some of the more excited ones leaped to the stage, and for a moment Will was not sure if they were going to embrace Alleyn or kill him. It was the player himself who saved the situation by thrusting himself upright from the crooked position of Richard and walking forward, in that gesture becoming once more Alleyn the actor.

To calm the crowd he spoke a few words of thanks, held out his hand to William Shakespeare, still in his costume of Lord Hastings, and introduced him to the audience.

It was the first sweet moment of personal triumph for Will as he bowed and listened to the cheers for himself as author.

When the theatre was finally empty, the scene backstage was just as exciting. The players crowded around both Alleyn and Shakespeare, embracing them and complimenting them. The only dark and unhappy face was that of Robert Greene. Even though he was one of Henslowe's special writers for the Lord Strange Company, he had had no particular reason to be at the theatre that afternoon and Will guessed that he had come out of curiosity to see another man's play. If so, *Richard III* had only made him more miserable.

Will was still feeling the intoxication of being cheered when he walked out of the Rose and found Richard Burbage waiting for him. Immediately he detected the hurt beneath the smile on his friend's face, the suffering in his eyes. Will understood:

Richard had wanted so much to play the part that Alleyn had. Had he not helped to create the earlier role of Gloucester?

"I'll write other plays for you, I promise that," Will assured his friend.

Richard's smile was more genuine. "I know you will. We're both young and I'll have my chance yet. But this is your day, Will, a great day, and I do not begrudge it to you. You are a great playwright. Neither Marlowe's *Tamburlaine* nor his *Dr. Faustus* can ever match what I saw today."

They walked slowly down the street, speaking of *Richard III*. "After this, the name 'William Shakespeare' will be known throughout London. On a playbill it will draw large crowds, mark my words."

They had gone only a short way before they realized that there was someone hurrying behind them to catch up to them.

"Burbage! Wait, please. If this be, as I think it is, the author of *Richard III*, which I have just seen, I would be honored to have his acquaintance."

Richard was smiling with evident pleasure. "Will, this is the celebrated John Florio, the man who has written the Italian-English dictionary, *A World of Words.*"

Will bowed low, liking the man on sight for his charming smile and his bright, alert eyes. "It is I who am honored."

"Please," said Florio, "will you be my guests? I must meet my pupil, the Earl of Southampton, at THE MERMAID TAVERN. I am tutoring him in Italian. Will you join us in a glass of wine?"

"To celebrate such a day? In Will's honor, indeed, we will," Richard agreed.

The inn was nearby and once there Florio chose a table and signaled the tapster boy to bring the best wine. "My most noble lord, the Earl, is late. I am under his patronage. . . . Have you a patron, Master Shakespeare? No? How strange! You know, the Earl is most kindly disposed to men of letters." Florio looked straight at Will with unmistakable sincerity in his eyes. "Especially poets. Have you ever thought to turn your hand to poems or songs or sonnets, sir?"

"I have written a few songs," Will said, "but no poetry that I consider worthy of being read. If I do——"

"If you do, remember what I have just said. We men of letters need patrons as much as these lords need us to add luster to their reputations. I can assure you, you would find the Earl of Southampton a most generous man." Then he abruptly changed the subject. "I think, *signore*, that you have a most special understanding of the human heart and mind, to write of Richard as you did, with both hatred and pity."

At that moment they were interrupted by the appearance of three men—the Earl of Southampton, richly dressed, laughing gaily, and Thomas Kyd. But it was the third man at whom Will stared. This tall, handsome, auburn-haired man was only a few years older than Southampton, yet he carried himself with an air of royal dignity. This could only be the great, much-talked-about Earl of Essex! The man whose brilliance had won him a degree of Master of Arts from Cambridge when he was only fourteen, whose bravery in fighting in the Netherlands had won him the heart of England, whose personal charm and good looks had made him Queen Elizabeth's favorite. No wonder that the Earl of Southampton looked upon Essex with eyes of hero worship as he presented Florio, Richard and Will to him.

But Thomas Kyd was a writer and as such was more interested in William Shakespeare at this moment than anything else. "I saw your play this afternoon, Will. My lords, if you were not there, you missed an event that all London will be talking of tomorrow. I told Kit Marlowe an hour ago that he must now look to his laurels. Tamburlaine has been eclipsed by Richard."

The two earls looked at William with greater interest, and Southampton leaned forward in his chair. "Is it so, Will Shakespeare? I am glad, truly. I have not forgotten a small discourse you gave us, in this same room, on the seven ages of man. I said then that you had wit."

"You must see *Richard III*, my lord," Florio urged. "There is one scene in which the genius of the author is revealed. Listen!"

Will was embarrassed as he listened to Florio's account of the scene, but he was also pleased to note that Southampton was gazing at him in frank admiration, the former trace of conde- scension in his manner gone. Though the Earl of Essex had said nothing, his eyes were appraising Shakespeare. Now he spoke:

"You are right, my good Florio, and it is apparent that we must see this play. Will you speak to Ned Alleyn, Master Shake- speare, and tell him I wish to have a performance at Essex House next week, on Monday?"

"Certainly, my Lord. The company will be honored and I will be pleased." He spoke haughtily, for his instinct told him that as a man of intellect he must not appear humble before these two lords.

"Shakespeare tells me that he has also written a trifle of poetry." In his desire to help Will gain favor with Southampton, Florio was almost too persistent. "Would you care to hear some? Will you not oblige us, Master Shakespeare?"

"Do, good sir," the Earl of Southampton requested. "Some- thing of youth and love perhaps?"

Will was annoyed at being thus forced to perform like any court jester. Noticing a pretty barmaid approaching them with a bottle of ale in one hand, he smiled, reached out and caught her by the arm and addressed his poem to her:

> What is love? 'tis not hereinafter;
> Present mirth hath present laughter;
> What's to come is still unsure:
> In delay there lies no plenty;
> Then come kiss me, sweet-and-twenty,
> Youth's a stuff will not endure.

The maid giggled and blushed, Florio shouted his approval, Richard looked at his friend with pride and Kyd stared at Will in astonishment. Southampton cried, "Bravo!" and the Earl of Essex rose from his chair and bowed low in appreciation. His arrogance of manner had somewhat diminished and there was a slight personal warmth in the glance he bestowed on Will.

"Excellent," he said. "It should be put to music and I——"

Suddenly the door of THE MERMAID flew open and Christopher Marlowe stood there, breathing hard, laughing and sobbing as he tried to catch his breath. His clothes were cut and torn.

"I have had sport!" he cried out, staggering over to Kyd. "An old enemy of mine did accost me on the street and we fought. He was a better swordsman and had me pinned, when my good friend Thomas Watson came by and took him on and ran this man through." Then he swaggered over to the bar counter, seized a tankard of ale and drained it.

Duels, brawls and quarrels were common enough on the streets of London, but the five men were shocked at Marlowe's disregard for the death of a man and his total unconcern for his own safety. Kyd hastened to the bar to seize his friend by the arm. "You're drunk, Kit, and you were a fool to come here! The constables know your habits, and this is the first place they will look for you. You must hide."

But even as he spoke constable and guards filled the doorway. "You are under arrest, Master Marlowe," said the officer. "Come with us. You'll spend this night in Newgate Prison, where we already have Watson confined."

No one was in a mood for poetry or conversation after the unpleasant incident, and Florio and the two lords soon excused themselves. Richard and Will walked down to the Thames to take a boat across to the City.

Richard shook his head sadly. "How tragic that a mind and talent such as Marlowe's should be thrown away in street fights and the prisons of London."

Will was even more disturbed. There was nothing he could do to help Marlowe, yet it seemed ironic that, at the very moment when his own fortunes were soaring upward, Christopher Marlowe was plunging downward to his own ruin.

A few weeks later he heard that Marlowe and Watson had been released after they had pleaded self-defense and proved that the other man had attacked first. But Will remained convinced that the man he had admired so much and whose *Tam-*

burlaine had influenced him so greatly was rushing headlong into more and more trouble.

That winter of 1591, at the age of twenty-seven, William Shakespeare finished *The Comedy of Errors*. For the first time he actually had fun with the writing. It was a welcome change from serious historical dramas and he let himself go in a kind of jubilant, frothy wit, creating absurd situations and slapstick that produced great laughter. The story was a trivial one, concerning a pair of twins, separated at birth, who as young men lived in the same city and were mistaken for each other. Hilarity ensued when one was accused of what the other did, when the wife of one and the sweetheart of the other could not tell them apart— and their twin servants only complicated the plot further.

The play was joyfully received by the London audiences. Though it did not have the rich, full humor of his later plays, it did contain lines that forecasted the future genius of William Shakespeare.

The Comedy of Errors was another step up the ladder to success and fame. The gentlemen of the law courts especially applauded it when it was performed at the Middle Temple and at Gray's Inn. This teasing, punning language was just what they liked.

The Earl of Southampton was not present when it was played in the Middle Temple and Will did not regret it. He had deliberately not gone to Essex House for the performance of *Richard III*; it was not that he was ashamed of being an actor, but at the moment he preferred that Southampton think of him as a poet and dramatist rather than as a player.

As the Christmas season of 1591 approached, all the acting companies were on their mettle. It was Queen Elizabeth's custom to hold Christmas Revels, starting before Christmas and ending many months afterward, during which time she demanded the best entertainment that could be found. Besides the money paid to those selected to perform, there was the prestige and honor of being chosen to appear at court.

The Queen's Men had no new plays to offer her. The Lord Admiral's Men now had Marlowe to write for them, but the Queen, who disliked him for his treasonous ideas and his immoral conduct, banned his *Jew of Malta*. Greene, also with the same company, had two plays to offer: *Orlando* and *Friar Bacon*. The children of St. Paul's, for whom Lyly wrote, would sing and act and dance.

With Lord Strange's Company needing an excellent new play in order to compete, Alleyn turned to Shakespeare and begged him to turn out the very best that he could. Realizing that the nobility had a taste for comedy at that moment, Will wrote *The Taming of the Shrew*.

When the play was accepted by the Master of the Revels, the whole company sighed with relief—but Will was walking on air one moment and plunged into despair the next. Suppose the Queen did not like it? The effect on his reputation and the company's would be disastrous.

Though the plague struck London and many people fled to the country, the acting companies could not leave. Elizabeth traveled from one of her palaces to another, but the actors had to be ready to go to Whitehall when she summoned them.

The call came for Lord Strange's Men on Twelfth Night. It was a splendid company of actors that set out that early evening for Whitehall, the most splendid of Elizabeth's town palaces. The company numbered many of the greatest actors in England: Edward Alleyn, Thomas Pope, Will Kempe, tall and elegant Augustine Phillips, blond and blue-eyed Henry Condell, William Sly, Richard Cowley, George Bryan, and William Shakespeare. To complete the splendid roster, Richard Burbage had just joined the troupe.

Traveling by boat on the Thames, the men disembarked at Whitehall stairs and were conducted by servants to the Master of Revels. He, in turn, led the players through a maze of courts and gardens into the palace and up to the Watching Chamber.

"You will wait here, please, until Her Royal Majesty is ready for your appearance," the Master commanded them.

The actors used the time to don their costumes, some putting on false beards, others inserting padding on their stomachs to make themselves stouter. A few carefully curled their mustaches to look more handsome and dashing. Robert Armin and Sim Crispian, the young boys who would be playing the female roles, were so nervous that they could not get into their skirts without help. In those days no woman was allowed on a stage. Young boys played all female parts.

Sounds of music—the flute, the recorder, the pipe, the viol—came from the adjoining Presence Chamber, prompting the actors to peek through a crack in the partly opened door. A ball was going on, but when it came Will's turn to look, he was so excited that the huge ballroom seemed nothing but a whirling peacock brilliance of colors and jewels.

The tension among the actors mounted until it was almost unbearable. It was with great relief that they heard the music stop: the waiting was over. Through the crack they could see the ballroom floor being cleared as the courtiers and ladies moved to seats along three sides of the room. Servants wheeled out a stage to the fourth side, directly in front of the Watching Chamber.

Then the Master returned with the admonition: "The Queen is ready. See to it you do not disappoint her."

The first two actors walked onstage and the play began. Will's romping, boisterous, witty story told of the marriage of madcap Petruchio to the bad-tempered, shrewish but beautiful Katharina and the ridiculous ways in which he tamed his bride. Both characters were high-spirited, clever, exuberant, and their clashes were just huge jokes that were supposed to evoke laughter.

The playwright was in agony. The first and second acts were nearly over: Why did not one single person in the court laugh? Was the comedy a complete failure?

Then came a shriek of laughter from the far side of the room where the Queen sat on her throne. At that her courtiers, who had not dared to so much as smile before and were containing their mirth as best they could, were free to laugh. Suddenly the whole room seemed to explode with chuckles and guffaws. Katharina and Petruchio were such a rollicking, unsentimental couple that the royal audience loved them, were charmed by them, even as they roared with laughter at them.

The play ended successfully, with Elizabeth gustily leading the court applause. Only then was Will free to catch a glimpse of the Queen. She was at the far end of the long hall and he could barely distinguish the tiny figure in a dazzling white gown, the jeweled bodice cut low, the great hooped skirts spreading across the throne. That head of bright orange-red hair was unmistakable.

When the actors were back in the other chamber and getting out of their costumes, the Lord Chamberlain came in. As the actors bowed low, he addressed them loftily:

"Her Majesty wishes me to extend her compliments both to the acting and to the play itself. It has pleased her well. Her Majesty wishes me to say further that it is the best performance at her Revels this year."

The men had to behave in decorous fashion, soberly thank the Lord Chamberlain, receive the money to be divided among them—and wait until they were on the barge going home before they could give vent to their feelings in cheers and hurrahs. William Shakespeare and his *Taming of the Shrew*, plus the acting of Ned Alleyn, Richard Burbage and young Robert Armin, had captured the prize honors of the year.

Now that it was over, the reaction set in. During the next week Will was tired, drained of energy and inspiration. The plague was raging in London. Everywhere he looked he saw people ill, suffering, dying. All night long carts rumbled through the streets with their ghastly burden of dead, being taken out of the City to be burned. The theatres were closing and he felt too exhausted to go on tour.

Will was filled with a sudden longing to go to Stratford and see his family. Why not? The change was just what he needed to restore his spirits.

11

It was a homecoming of great rejoicing. Anne, his brothers and sisters ran out into the street to welcome and embrace him; his mother and father waited in the doorway, with three children behind them peeping out at this strange man who was their father. In a few moments they were over their fear and clamoring to be held. With Susanna in one arm, he put the other around his mother and held her close, seeing how gray her hair was but how straight she still held herself. John Shakespeare thumped his son on the back with such happiness in his face that he looked as merry-cheeked as of old.

It was a long time before the household quieted down. As they all gathered before the fire, Will relaxed, letting the ease and familiar ways of the old house soothe him, drive out the last drop of London tension. He was home.

John Shakespeare looked at the ten pounds his son had placed in his hands and marveled. Will had earned it by acting before the Queen and writing a play for her. Anne was happy at his success, but it was his mother who was the proudest. Will was realizing the promise she had always seen in him.

There was much excitement as the family unwrapped Will's presents—a green silk dress for Anne, a filagree brooch for his mother, toys for the children and a silver buckle for Gilbert.

Later he drew his father aside and they talked of business.

"With the money from work done in the shop and the money you have sent us, we are doing as well as can be expected," John Shakespeare told him. "Some of the debts are paid. But . . ."

"I know. It is Asbies you still want, Father. You'll have it, I promise."

Will decided to remain at home for several months and do some writing as soon as he settled down a bit. He made friends with his children and had long talks about them with Anne. He also began work on another play, *The Two Gentlemen of Verona*, but in a short while he put it aside to do something that had been on his mind since Richard Field and John Florio had mentioned it to him. He began writing poetry.

Since it was in the fashion of the day to write of love, Will chose to tell the story of Venus and Adonis in verse. In London the flow of poetry had not been as natural as it seemed to be in Stratford, where even the winter's snows were beautiful. His mind was full of songs and the wonder of nature.

In writing the long poem, feelings held in check for years, almost forgotten in the furious struggle of work, were stirred and brought to life again. Youthful and romantic longings surged through him. He and Anne had a deep and constant affection for each other, the bond between them was strong, and the children were theirs to cherish. Therefore his yearning had no reality, no face, no special woman's smile or laugh . . . it was a yearning for the loveliness of romance.

Late in the summer of 1592 *Venus and Adonis* was finished. Word had come that the plague had died down and the theatres would soon be opening again. It was time for Will to return to London.

He said nothing of the poem when he reached the City, but quietly resumed the writing of his unfinished play. He was immediately sought after for many roles, and was glad of the money because he had insisted that his mother and Anne have a nurse to help with the children. He finished *The Two Gentlemen of Verona* and was pleased with its success.

Though he worked and wrote, he was waiting for one man to come back to London—the Earl of Southampton.

Robert Greene died in August of that year. He had thrown away his own brilliance, and envy at others' success had consumed him. During his last days he was able to buy food and drink only by selling a pamphlet that described how the thieves of London stole and robbed and killed men for pennies—the very thieves in whose house he lived as he lay dying

Greene had also written another pamphlet entitled A *Groats Worth of Wit Bought with a Million of Repentance*. After his death Henry Chettle, a publisher, printed it, thus bringing down upon his head a storm of reproach because it contained a scurrilous, lying attack on William Shakespeare. Greene had made an attempt to win Marlowe and Kyd to his side by describing Will as "an upstart crow, beautified with our feathers, that with his tiger's heart wrapt in a players hide, supposes he is as well able to bumbast out a blank verse as the best of you . . ." And had gone on to sneer at Shakespeare as a stagehand.

When Will learned that everyone was talking and laughing about Greene's tract, he was deeply hurt. His pride, always sensitive to slights, suffered terribly under the accusation that he stole from other men's plays and made bumbling attempts at writing blank verse, turning out poor imitations of better men's work. Although his name was not mentioned in Greene's posthumous attack, the reference to the tiger's heart unquestionably identified the author of *Henry VI*, since they were a parody of Shakespeare's own words.

Marlowe was furious about the pamphlet for he did not consider Will's plays copies or thefts. Going to Chettle, Kit demanded he make an apology. The publisher was greatly disturbed and went to the theatre to speak to Will. He was so impressed by Shakespeare's gentlemanly manner and his intelligence that he not only wrote the apology but also made public his own opinion of Will: "as civil in demeanor as he was excellent in the writing of plays, and upright in all his dealings." The laughter at Will's expense ceased. In fact, the apology brought him excellent publicity and his name became even more well known to the people of London.

One day he met John Florio on the street and learned that the Earl of Southampton had returned to London. He carefully wrapped up his long poem *Venus and Adonis* and sat down to write the Earl the letter that would accompany it. Rarely had he worked so hard over a speech in his play as he worked over that letter. It read:

> I know not how I shall offend in dedicating my unpolished lines to your Lordship, nor how the world will censure me for choosing so strong a prop to support so weak a burthen; only if your Honor seem but pleased, I account myself highly praised, and vow to take advantage of all idle hours, till I have honored you with some grave labour. But if the first heir of my invention prove deformed, I shall be sorry it had so noble a god-father: and never after ear so barren a land, for fear it yield me still so bad a harvest, I leave it to your Honorable survey, and your Honor to your heart's content which I wish may always answer your own wish, and the world's hopeful expectation.
>
> Your Honors in all duty,
William Shakespeare

An answer was not long in coming. The next day an equerry in the handsome livery of the Earl, wearing a haughty look on his face, called at the Rose Theatre and requested Will to accompany him. His manner showed how little he liked the business of walking the streets with a man who still bore the smear of grease paint on his cheek.

Will was ushered into the long gallery of Southampton's house and welcomed by the nobleman himself with outstretched hand.

"Shakespeare! By my faith." The Earl's face was flushed with pleasure and his eyes were dancing in his youthful face. "It is I who am honored to have such lines dedicated to me. They are more beautiful than anything that Sydney or Spenser has written. They shall be published. I shall buy them in quantities and send them to all my friends."

"You are too kind, my lord." Will struggled to keep the elation out of his voice and face and remain smoothly controlled. The waiting had been worth it; his gamble had succeeded. Now that he had won the Earl's favor, there would only be renown and fortune ahead. Any benefit the creative artist received from the patron was more than offset by the advantages the patron received. To be an important figure at court, a nobleman must be known either for his valor in war or for his patronage of literature and the arts. There was no war at present; John Florio had hinted to Will that the Earl of Southampton needed the glory of a poet's work to add luster and brilliance to his name. As much as Will needed a patron, his patron needed to boast about "his" William Shakespeare even more.

But nothing of this could be said openly. "My gracious lord," he murmured, "I tender you my service. If I have written anything of worth, it is nothing to what I shall write for you someday, and it is only worthy because the Earl of Southampton deigns to receive it." But he could not help adding: "But to return to the verses, did this tale of love please you? Ah, my lord." He laughed. "You are blushing. You should be thinking of your studies, of philosophy and grave subjects, not of love."

For a second it seemed as if the Earl would be insulted at the liberty Will was taking. Then good spirits triumphed over formality and he threw his head back and laughed. "Will Shakespeare, we shall be friends! I am Henry Wriothesley to you and you are Will Shakespeare to me. There must be no 'my lord' between us—I forbid it. Since I first heard you talk in THE MERMAID I enjoyed your company, I admired your charm of manners and your wit. There was so much wisdom in what you said——"

"Then let me be your counselor as well as friend," Will told him. "I am ten years older than you."

The Earl seated himself on a cushioned window seat and motioned for Will to sit beside him. "Nevertheless, you are young enough to understand youth. John Florio is a fine man but so studious, so solemn. He could never write with the passion and fire you reveal in your poem. I plan to have a small gathering here one evening this week, and you must be my guest. *Venus and Adonis* shall be read aloud and what a triumph it will be!"

"Richard Burbage could read it very well, if it please you,"

Will suggested. He leaned back on the comfortable seat, enjoying the splendor of this gallery with its long, tall, narrow windows and polished oak walls hung with pictures and tapestries. He gazed in admiration at two white marble statues of Roman goddesses framing a doorway. The wealth around him was dazzling after the meagerness of his own little room.

"Excellent," the Earl said. "Will you ask Burbage for me? It will be on Friday night, at eight o'clock. And in the summer when I visit my country estate of Titchfield, you must come with me. There will be a fine company of friends present."

He walked to the gardens with Will when it was time to go. "Please, Will, I ask that you be my counselor as well as my friend, as you have offered. I would like to discuss certain problems with you—things I cannot discuss with the Earl of Essex or with Florio. Did you know, for instance, that my mother is already selecting someone for me to marry and I am resisting?" Then his manner abruptly changed and he was the patron once more. "You must ask of me what you will. I am in your debt. My purse strings are open to you, though I have not received my inheritance yet and must remain on an allowance for a few more years."

"I am more than repaid by your willingness to accept my dedication."

London, the whole world, had changed for Will as he walked back to his lodgings. No longer would he be unknown. No longer need he worry about the next shilling. In one day his fortune and his future were golden and he was the friend of a lord. Will passed the tailor shop where he had purchased his first suit of clothes in London; he turned back and recklessly ordered fine forest green silk to be made into doublet and breeches, a new white ruff, a cloak of black velvet trimmed with silver. The tailor promised to have the new clothes ready by Friday.

He felt wildly excited and, after so many years of sober, hardworking thrift, he wanted to do foolish, extravagant things. The Earl of Southampton would reward him—if *Venus and Adonis* were truly as excellent as they thought—and even if Will had to wait for the better part of it, there would surely be something forthcoming immediately.

And so it proved. The next day handsome gifts arrived at Will's lodgings: gold buckles for belt and shoes, a heavy gold chain, a large leather box from Italy inlaid with mosaics and filled to the brim with gold coins.

"When the rest comes," Will promised Richard Burbage, "we will use it for the theatre you and I have spoken of so many times. Our *own* theatre and freedom from Henslowe!"

A good portion of the money in the leather box he sent on to Stratford, feeling very happy that from now on they would not have to pinch and struggle so hard.

That Friday night when he reached the steps of Southampton's mansion, Will Shakespeare was nervous but he hoped his quick eye would stand him in good stead. He knew that his clothes were suitable. If they were not as rich and opulent as the others, he did not worry: he was not pretending to be a lord. But he hoped that the good manners he had learned at home would be sufficient, for he did not want to disgrace either himself or his new patron.

Inside, Will soon found himself amid a gay and elegant collection of lords and ladies. The glimpse he had once caught of the Queen's Chamber had been a blur of color and sounds. Here he saw on a slightly smaller scale the same rainbow of colors, heard the same sounds of music and laughter. The difference was that now he was actually a part of it. How wonderful it all seemed! He found it intoxicating to be so close to these beautiful, high-born women, gowned in silks and satins of every color, gliding about the great hall, gesturing with fans to display dazzling jewels on wrists and arms.

Will stood beside Florio, watching. Lights from a thousand candles sparkled on jewels and reflected the radiance of diamonds and amethyst, emerald and opal, pearl and sapphire, dimming even the fine golden vase that stood on a cabinet against the wall.

His eye went from one girl to another: here was one whose

blonde curls worn high and back from her forehead were intertwined with a rope of pearls. Here was another whose hair had been dyed to imitate the Queen's; as she walked by with her hand on a courtier's arm, a wave of perfume came from a golden ball that swung at her waist. Another kept peeking into her fan of tiny mirrors to see if the perfection of her oval face were really without flaw.

Then Will saw *the* one girl. She was dark and taller than the others. She wore a white satin gown with the skirt embroidered in seed pearls designed to represent the sun, the moon and the stars. The ruff around her slim neck was not pleated, it was a flaring shell of the purest and finest lace. She looked directly at him and smiled, a mocking, gay smile that he would never forget for the rest of his life. She continued to talk to the Earl of Oxford, but her eyes kept straying back to Will.

The Dark Lady. Her real name he locked inside his heart as Florio whispered it to him. She remained always his Dark Lady.

The music changed to a madrigal and the guests danced. Southampton found the place he wanted—two chairs in a prominent position—and brought Will over to sit by his side. When the music stopped, his chamberlain announced the reading of *Venus and Adonis*. The guests took chairs along the walls, leaving a space in the middle of the ballroom, and Richard Burbage stepped out.

The poem was the glorious triumph the Earl had expected, and more. After the first few minutes the roomful of people could not be still. Involuntary cries of delight and surprise broke out, clapping and excited wavings of fans interrupted the reading as Richard's audience grew more and more excited. "Charming! Divinely charming!" cried one pert girl, a Maid of Honor to the Queen. "Oh, do hush!" her companion urged. "I want to hear." "Oh, I could weep for Venus, so unloved!" cried another. There would be a momentary silence to permit Richard to speak a few more lines, then another noisy outburst of approval.

Finally the Earl stood up and raised a graceful hand. "No more tonight," he said, ignoring all protests and pleas. "The poem is being printed and you may all read it at your leisure. Let me now present the author of this magnificent work." He gestured to Shakespeare to rise.

As Will bowed, he saw not these guests, but his stern, proper Arden aunts—"Your manners, William!"—and he made the deepest, most courtly bow of his life.

The audience once more broke up into small chattering groups and Will turned to find the Dark Lady at his side. Afterward he could not remember exactly what words they spoke to each other. She complimented him, but teasingly; he found the courage to answer her in the same light vein. And then they continued to play a game of this sort, tossing light insults back and forth as they strolled in front of a tapestry that hung from ceiling to floor. For Will this was a delightful moment—he felt like a youth again. Never had he met such a creature . . . a girl who did not look demure but gazed directly and challengingly into his eyes, a girl whose wit was sharp, whose laugh was forthright and gay, whose tenderness only sometimes appeared in the soft curve of her smile. The fact that she had singled him out and had spoken to him heightened the glory and success of the evening.

The shabbiness of his own poor quarters when he arrived home early the next morning did not bother him at all. He was still seeing Southampton's elated and proud face. He was still hearing the Earl of Essex's quick desire to have people know that "I have already had the pleasure of Master Shakespeare's acquaintance!" Best of all, he could go to sleep with the face of the Dark Lady filling his dreams.

He realized that he was far beneath her station, and of course he was married, the father of three children. She was young and rich and would one day marry some nobleman. But he could not shut her completely out of his heart and thoughts. Perhaps his poetry and his quick wit had attracted her. He had no idea that he, William Shakespeare, at twenty-eight, possessed the irresistible qualities of the dreamy poet and the strong man of resolution. The small, narrow mustache he now wore gave him a slightly dashing air. His chestnut hair curled slightly back from his forehead. Without being aware of it, he was a man of sensitive, romantic appearance.

When Will awoke later that day he was no longer the gallant courtier. Once more the serious actor and writer, he reported to the Rose Theatre as usual for rehearsals. Although he continued to work hard, the Earl of Southampton had meant it when he asked Will to be his friend, and the two men met frequently to spend a pleasant evening boating on the Thames or strolling in the magnificent gardens of Essex House. Gradually Will found himself accepted by Southampton's friends, particularly the Earl of Essex.

When the plague struck London, worse than ever, the theatres were closed by law. "Come to Titchfield with us," Southampton urged. "We will have an amusing group of friends but, when you wish to write, no one will bother you. My mother is visiting elsewhere, and we will have the house to ourselves."

Will had thought to go to Stratford but wisdom told him not to refuse his patron's generous invitation.

~~~~~ 12 ~~~~~

The Earl of Southampton, his tutor Florio and Will Shakespeare set out one fine morning for Titchfield, accompanied by equerries and grooms. Other servants rode ahead to see that their accommodations at inns along the way were the very best. With each passing mile Will felt the years and troubles and worries drop from his shoulders, and with each passing hour his liking for the Earl deepened into an affection that became a strong bond between them. Will looked upon the nobleman almost as a younger brother. Despite his lordly airs, Southampton was gentle, good and kind.

Arriving at Titchfield, a country estate of great splendor, the Earl led his guests through a great hall with a magnificent fireplace, tapestried walls and mullioned windows, thronelike chairs, benches covered with cushions of exquisite needlework in vivid colors. When Will was shown into his large bedroom, he stared in amazement at the four-poster bed hung with yellow silk curtains and the walls covered in red damask. He gazed at the heavy coverlet embroidered with the Southampton coat of arms, then wandered over to the windows and stood looking down at the velvety expanse of lawn, the flower gardens, the small lake where swans floated and the forest where deer waited the hunters. The magnificence of the place was more than he had ever imagined it could be.

Below, the Earl stood in eager conversation with his head forester. Dogs leaped and jumped around him, baying in eagerness for the hunt. Around his wrist was the leather thong that held the feet of his favorite falcon, ruffling great wings in its desperate desire to soar skyward. Then Will's attention abruptly shifted as a rider swept into the courtyard attended by a train of horsemen following behind as if it were his own private army.

Southampton hurried forward to welcome the Earl of Essex.

That evening there were just four of them, Essex, Southampton, Florio and himself. In the weeks to come other gentlemen and noble lords visited the Earl, and Essex periodically disappeared when the Queen commanded his presence at one of her palaces, but he always returned. Will enjoyed himself most when the four of them were there alone. Essex relaxed and showed the best side of his nature during those times. No wonder he was Elizabeth's favorite. Handsome, talented, fearless, openhearted, Essex could captivate anyone. The Earl of Southampton was his devoted worshiper, Florio his great admirer, and as William Shakespeare looked at him and listened to him, he also felt admiration—and only now and then grave doubts.

For the Earl of Essex could be as willful as he was wonderful. He could be recklessly impatient and bold. If he could not have his own way, at times, he would sulk as foolishly as a child, planning revenges that were mean and petty. This side, however, was revealed in rare flashes of temper. For the most part his presence was something to look forward to, and the four men spent long hours out-of-doors during the day, long hours talking and laughing around the fireplace in the evenings.

One such evening, as they all stretched their feet out toward the blazing fire, luxuriating in the comfort and ease after a day's hard but invigorating chase through forest and upland meadows, with horses and hounds racing after the fleet deer, comfortable after a hearty dinner of roast beef, choice capon, mutton and pastries, the talk turned to the young host's marriage.

"Whom will you marry, Southampton?" asked Essex. "She must be good, she must be rich, she must be young—above all she must be beautiful."

" 'Tis beauty that doth make women proud," objected Will.

"Then if not beautiful," jested Florio, "let her be sweet as an angel."

Will pretended to be scornful. He got up, walked to the fireplace and leaned his elbow on it. He looked down at them. "All women are angels, wooing; once married, they can turn into fiends. Shall we allow our poor Southampton to marry, to be miserable, to lose such good company as ours? Because we well know that after marriage the wife will not permit the husband to spend all his days in the hunt, to come home with muddy boots . . . to sit like this with his friends and talk of philosophy and weighty matters. . . . No, our poor lord will have to dance attendance on his lady's pleasure and be perfumed and daintily dressed at all times and tell her all evening how pretty she is, help her match the silks for her embroidery, and beg her leave to curse awhile."

At such a description the others roared with laughter, while the Earl of Southampton gasped in mock fright. "I must be protected against such a fate! What shall we do? Can we not sign a pledge that none of us will speak to a woman? We will spend our time, instead, in earnest study, cultivating our talents in the arts, or fling ourselves into rude, manly sports."

Essex seized on the idea. "We will post sentries all around Titchfield and not let any woman enter. We will save Southampton from his terrible fate and we ourselves will become grave, serious, learned men. This will be our second university, our sanctuary against the follies and whimsies of females."

"Even against the Queen?" Southampton asked what neither Florio nor Shakespeare would have presumed to say, even in fun.

Essex groaned. "Who is more truly female, capricious, more whimsical, more fickle and changeable than our Queen?"

Suddenly, while the others in mock seriousness played upon this theme and invented more and more rules for their behavior in this womanless society, Will saw the whole thing as a marvelous comic play. He was grateful when shortly afterward Southampton yawned and suggested that they retire. Once in his own room, Will called for the servant to bring him candles, quills and paper. All that night he wrote, staggering to bed at dawn and sending word to the Earl that he would not join the hunt that day.

Nor did he the next nor the next. He even found that taking his meals with the others interfered with what was on his mind. Their chatter and laughter, their curious questions about what he was doing, annoyed him. He was rude to his patron, but Southampton took it well, secretly proud that Shakespeare was writing something under his roof.

Will called his play *Love's Labour's Lost*. It was a story of a king and three of his lords, Biron, Longaville and Dumain, who vowed to live for three years without speaking to a woman, to spend their time in study and grave discourses, to fast one day in a week, eat one meal a day and sleep three hours a night, disciplining their bodies so that their minds might benefit.

Almost before the experiment started, a princess, attended by her ladies, arrived at the king's court to make a special plea. He could not be rude and had to suspend the rules for the time being, though the men were determined to speak to the ladies only out of courtesy and for business—but no more.

Naturally, the king fell in love with the princess, each of his lords with one of the ladies. First Biron wandered into the park, thinking of his secret love; he hid when the king came by, reading aloud a poem to the princess. In turn, the king hid as the other two lords declared their love; then all four realized that their vows were foolish.

An attempt they made to play a joke on the ladies was turned on them, and the princess gained the upper hand. When the king and the lords asked their hands in marriage, they were given a year's task of hard study and work among the sick and the unfortunate before they could come back to claim their loves. Even with this serious ending it was a blithe, merry tale, full of wit and humor.

Will finished the play in little over a week, working day and night. All his meals were carried to him on trays and kept warm in covered dishes; the candles provided him were fat, tall ones.

But though such comforts helped, Will was unaware of them. He did not read the notes Southampton sent him, nor did he hear the gay company as they shouted to him beneath his windows to join them on horseback.

When it was done he slept for a whole day. Then he walked in the garden, lonely, empty and weak from exhaustion.

That night he read his play to Southampton, Florio, the Earl of Essex and two other gentlemen. They laughed so hard that they could not keep from interrupting him.

"That Armado!"—a minor character but John Florio thought him the funniest in the whole play—"that pompous, conceited popinjay of a Spaniard with his fancy, overblown speech!"

"It is Rosaline and Katharine who please me most," Essex said. "You have given the ladies much the best of it, Will."

"Read on," the others urged.

When he had finished the reading, Shakespeare was toasted with tall glasses of wine, his play was praised. Their honest delight in him and in his work brought him out of fatigue and made him feel *this* labor, at least, was not lost. Never had he thought himself to be so happy as he was that evening, surrounded by his friends.

The next day came word from London that the plague had lessened and the theatres were reopening. The group broke up, Southampton going with Essex to the court of the Queen, and Will and Florio returning to London.

En route they talked of the two lords. "The Earl of Southampton has a generous nature," Florio said, "but he is so easily swayed that I hope no harm comes to him. Perhaps he will find a glorious future with the Earl of Essex."

"How do you mean, Florio?"

"Everyone speaks of Essex as the natural heir to the throne, since he is Elizabeth's cousin and her favorite. She has only to name him as the next King of England and he will be so. He is counting on it, mind my words. He is impatient that she says and does nothing, while up in Scotland sits James I, who may succeed unless the Queen stirs herself to name Essex."

Will, too, had heard such rumors but he had not realized that the Earl of Essex was actually expecting to succeed to the throne. "If that happened," he said slowly, "the people of England would rejoice. They love him. He's colorful and brave, but . . ."

"But what, my dear Shakespeare?"

"But I do not know. I, too, am caught by his grace and gallantry. But for king-becoming graces—justice, temperance, steadfastness, verity, perseverance—I know not how much of these he has. Perhaps I am wrong. Certainly our Good Queen Bess does not possess them overmuch, yet she is good and great. I hope my doubts are wrong and that Essex would make a fine king . . . certainly he would be better than what we hear of James in Scotland."

The theatres that had reopened were again closed quickly as the plague flared up and raced through the City once more. This time Will went to Stratford and settled down to write a new play. He did not work with such intensity this time, but allowed himself hours to play with Susanna and Hamnet and Judith and to talk with his mother and father and Anne, who never tired of hearing about the wonders of Titchfield. The family proudly spread the word through Stratford that William Shakespeare, the scapegrace son, the wanderer, was now the personal friend of the greatest lords in all England.

The new play, *Romeo and Juliet*, was taken from an old Italian play Will had read as a boy. It would be a love story, tender and tragic. It was not yet finished when Will learned that, in spite of the plague, the Queen intended to hold her Revels. Lord Strange's Men assembled quickly in London to rehearse any new play they could find. A messenger was dispatched to Stratford to ask Will if he had a new play.

Before he left, taking *Love's Labour's Lost* with him, he and his wife discussed the possibility of her moving with the children to London. Both decided against the idea, for then Will would have had to support two homes instead of one. Furthermore,

Anne was reluctant, being timid about strange places and ways and new people.

Love's Labour's Lost was chosen by the Master of the Revels, and so well did it please the Queen that, after seeing it on December 27, she insisted that it be played again for her on January 6. This time Will saw Her Majesty clearly. The troupe had been asked to wait in the outer chamber after the performance, and the men could see Elizabeth, followed by her Lord Chamberlain, slowly pacing in front of the door, which had been left open. The Queen looked in and though all the actors were kneeling they heard her whisper a question and Will, daring to raise his head, saw that she was looking directly at him and smiling.

In his eyes she was beautiful, though actually she was small, pockmarked and brightly rouged. Her scanty hair was dyed red, her gorgeous brocade satin gown much too young and pretty for a fifty-eight-year-old woman. What he saw was the real Elizabeth, the great, warm, forceful personality of his Queen.

The plague ran its course and slowly loosened its murderous hold on the City. People came back a few at a time, shop windows were full again, shutters on houses were flung open and the men of the theatre began to gather in London. Will moved to a more comfortable house, where he could have a fire on chill evenings and could write more easily. He continued to work on *Romeo and Juliet*, acting whenever a performance was given by the Lord Strange group.

While Will's own affairs were progressing so well, Marlowe was in trouble again. The authorities had searched the rooms that Marlowe shared with Thomas Kyd and had found a set of handbills that criticized the government, as well as some copies of a pamphlet that was antireligious in tone. Since Marlowe was not there and Kyd was, the police arrested him.

Will, who had always liked Kyd, was worried, and was immensely relieved to answer a knock on his door one evening and find Kyd standing there. But his relief changed to anxiety again when he looked into his friend's grief-stricken face.

"What has happened? When were you released?" Will asked.

Kyd told him the story. Even though the incriminating papers had not been his, he had kept silent and remained in prison. That day, May 31, he had been released—because Marlowe was dead and now Kyd could tell the truth because it could hurt his friend no longer.

"He was killed in a drunken brawl," said Kyd sadly, "with Frizer, a swindler and a cheat, and Robert Poley, whom some say is a secret agent spying on Marlowe. Kit and Frizer began to quarrel over the bill at a tavern in Deptford. Kit snatched Frizer's dagger away from him and slashed at him, and in the struggle that followed, Frizer thrust it into Marlowe's head. He was killed instantly."

Both men were silent, thinking to themselves that it was a mean and sordid way for a great poet and playwright to die.

With Marlowe's death the era dominated by the university wits came to an end. Greene was already dead; the playwright Thomas Lodge was traveling abroad; Kyd was to write less and less; Sir Walter Raleigh was to completely lose royal favor by falling in love with and marrying one of her Maids of Honor, against Elizabeth's wishes.

The star that was rising steadily, shining more brightly every year, was that of William Shakespeare.

His poem *Venus and Adonis* was published that year, 1593, by Richard Field. The first printing sold out immediately and so did the second and the third; in fact, Field had to put through nine printings.

"So are you to be a poet and not a playwright, Will?" asked Richard Burbage. The two friends were walking along the Thames, one summer day, relishing the somewhat cleaner air and trying to forget the horrible stench of the City streets, where the plague still lingered.

Shakespeare shook his head. "No, although I am now writing another poem, my real work is in the theatre. But what is to become of the players' companies, Richard? Will they all come back to London?"

"I don't know. They are hard hit. My father now has the Admiral's Men at the Theatre; the Queen's Men have virtually disappeared. I think it will be a mixture of Lord Strange's and Lord Admiral's that takes to the road this year."

To everyone's horror, the plague broke out again with renewed fury in 1594. Will hastened to Stratford and safety. His new poem, *Lucrece*, also dedicated to the Earl of Southampton, was published with great success by Richard Field. Will was grateful for the money Field sent him and for the lavish gifts that were delivered to Stratford by one of the Earl's messengers.

He had seen Southampton only once before leaving London. They had gone to a ball together and again Will had met and talked and laughed with his Dark Lady.

That she liked him, he knew, but he had seen her flirt and talk with other men, and now the pleasure of his romantic feelings for her was tinged with unreasonable jealousy.

In Stratford, at least, there were no such tormenting emotions and he could write. His children were growing up. His son Hamnet was his deep pride, though he dearly loved the saucy Susanna and the quiet, pretty Judith. Anne was content to have her husband with her for such a long time. He rejoiced to see his mother laugh more often and his father jaunty again.

After he finished *Romeo and Juliet*, more satisfied with it than he had been with any other play, he began *A Midsummer Night's Dream*. With forest and meadow so close, reviving memories of childhood and youth, it was natural that Will should turn to these for inspiration. The forest had always been an enchanted place to him, and wandering in it he forgot the sadness of Marlowe's death, the tragedies of the plague and even the foolishness of his jealousy. They belonged to London. Here he felt lighthearted and so this new play wove in his mind a fairy tale of delicate beauty and rich, earthly humor.

Nothing disturbed that mood. He walked the paths and songs sang themselves in his head. He sat on mossy stones beneath the oaks and wrote of love, of magic spells, of fairy sprites, of nonsense and whimsy. He remembered the old tales of Richard Hathaway and put the fairy king and queen into this play.

Will even remembered the servants at his Arden aunts' the day they gave their amateur play, and they found their way into his story.

By the end of May, 1594, the plague had ended. Twenty thousand people had died in London and in nearby towns but the big city was rapidly pulling itself together again and more than anything else its citizens wanted to be entertained, to forget the horrors of the epidemic.

Shakespeare returned to find that Lord Strange had died, as had his son, and the company had no patron.

Richard Burbage and Will discussed the problem. Who would be their new patron? What company could they assemble? "Money is needed, Will," said Burbage, "to buy plays and costumes and scenery. If we had that, I am sure I could win the favor of some lord. In fact, I have someone powerful in mind. But where will we get the money?"

"Let me think about it, Richard," Will told him. "I'm as anxious as you to have our own company."

Even though the two men had not found a solution, *Romeo and Juliet* was performed that same week by a hastily gathered group of actors. With young Armin as Juliet and Burbage as Romeo, no better performance could have been given by an established, well-organized company. Shakespeare was also in the cast, playing the part of Mercutio, Romeo's close friend.

This new play moved the audience more deeply than any other that had ever appeared in London. It told the tragic, age-less, incomparably tender story of the forbidden love between a boy and a girl, and how they died for each other.

For the first time since William Shakespeare had been acting, he heard an incredible sound from the audience. People in every part of the theatre were weeping, sobbing, as they watched the drama on the stage. How could they hold back their tears when

Romeo looked down at the beautiful girl he believed to be dead, and murmured:

> Ah! dear Juliet,
> Why art thou yet so fair? Shall I believe
> That unsubstantial death is amorous;
> And that the lean abhorred monster keeps
> Thee here in dark to be his paramour?
> For fear of that, I will still stay with thee;
> And never from this palace of dim night
> Depart again . . .

Will did not need the applause from the spectators nor the extravagant compliments backstage to know that *Romeo and Juliet* was a tremendous success and a magnificent play. He admitted to himself, modestly but honestly, that his talents were growing steadily, that his writing revealed his mastery of the craft.

What concerned him more was the need for an acting company and a theatre to play in. An idea had taken root in his mind the first time that he and Richard Burbage had discussed the matter, and finally he decided to act upon it. The Earl of Southampton had promised to reward him handsomely when he received his inheritance, and although Will had not seen his patron since returning to London, he knew that the young nobleman had come into his fortune in recent times. Now was the moment to ask.

~~~ 13 ~~~

Shakespeare sent a message to the Earl of Southampton, requesting an audience. Within an hour a servant brought him the reply:

> Come at once, dear Will. May I appoint the time for this afternoon at one of the clock, and the place to be Ely Place in Holborn?

Upon arriving at the appointed place, Will found it to be a tournament ground, a training school for swordsmen and fencers, as well as a practice yard for those who did not wish to lose their skill and agility with the blade. Ely Place was ringed with thirty or more spectators watching a duel in the center of the yard. Strolling over to look, Will saw that it was Southampton joyfully challenging the Earl of Essex, a magnificent swordsman. Even though Southampton was compelled to give ground, he appeared to be happy to be engaged in this contest with his idol.

The two fought back and forth over the courtyard stones, their rapiers flashing in the sun. Finally Essex pressed close, forcing Southampton further back and, just when victory was assured, he stepped back and raised his weapon high. "A fair match, Southampton," he cried. "I'll not take advantage of you. The sun is in your eyes."

Laughing, the two friends cast their weapons aside. The man in the plumed hat shouted, "Bravo, Essex! You are generous as well as brave."

While Will waited for Southampton to change from his fencing costume, he noticed how everyone clustered around Essex, praising him, flattering him. In all England there were only a few who opposed him. Unfortunately for Essex, two of those men were the Cecils, father and son. The father had long been Elizabeth's foremost adviser and now the son was taking his place. Both were the exact opposite of Essex: prudent, cautious, restrained men, guiding England in the ways of peace, not yielding to threats of war and temptations to invade other countries for glory and power. Essex hated the Cecils and was furious that Elizabeth should call him her "favorite" but turn to them for advice.

The Earl of Southampton soon came out to join Will. A moment before he had been a swordsman; now he was a dandy. "What would you have, my dear friend?" He took Will's arm and they walked slowly to a bench. "I hope it is a favor? You have let me do so little to show my appreciation."

Will carefully explained the problems of the actors, who were without sponsor, organization or money. "Most of us would like to be free of Henslowe, but we need a large sum of money to set up our own company."

"Say no more." Southampton put his hand on Will's arm. "I shall be honored. I have been greatly in your debt since the dedication of the poem *Lucrece* has made me the envy of London." He looked kindly at Will. "The sonnets you have been sending me, in lieu of letters, have put me under more obligation. In them you have advised and counseled me, chided me when I needed it, given me of your great wisdom and affection . . . even revealed some of your own secret thoughts."

Those sonnets, sent to Southampton when one or the other was away, were indeed part of their private correspondence, never intended for publication.

"But, Will, you must be understanding and patient if I do not see you as much as I once did, or if I think less and less about poetry. I am a man now, and it is my duty to think of my house and my country. I must busy with matters of war."

A premonition seized Will. "But we are not at war!"

"We should be!" In a passion of anger the younger man's hand moved to the hilt of his rapier. "We should make England's name a terror to all nations and carry the war into Spain. The Queen waits. She says yea and nay to Essex—and listens instead to that cautious old man Cecil and his hunchbacked son."

"Remember the Netherlands? The Armada?" Will wanted to fight this change in someone he still regarded as a carefree boy. "What with the plague, the gallows, the crimes of poverty, the intrigues at court, are not the men of England troubled enough, sir? Must we kill more in a war?"

"Ah, my dear friend, I mean this not contemptuously, but I was bred differently. To me, war is glorious. It is the way of ambition and pride and reward." Southampton lifted his head proudly. "Essex says he has need of men like me." Then he looked remorseful and once again became friendly. "Forgive me for speaking of my affairs when you come to me with yours. It will be a joy for me to help you, one of England's great poets and playwrights——"

"Not just of England." John Florio had come up quietly. "I think our Shakespeare, with *Romeo and Juliet*, now takes his place with the greatest of the world."

For a brief moment things were as they always had been. The three friends shared a warm affection, held together by strong bonds of respect, admiration, loyalty. Will was to remember that occasion in the days of grief and sorrow to come.

Three days later a purse arrived from the Earl containing one thousand pounds. It was more than enough for the immediate needs of the new company, so Will kept part of it for personal expenses and sent the rest to Stratford. Richard Burbage spoke to the Queen's Lord Chamberlain, who willingly agreed to lend the company his name and support.

At first the Lord Chamberlain's Men used Henslowe's theatre at Newington. During the month of June they acted *Titus Andronicus, The Taming of the Shrew* and Marlowe's *Jew of Malta*.

When James Burbage reopened the Theatre, Shakespeare and Richard moved the Lord Chamberlain's Men there.

Almost the first play they put on at the Theatre was one that Will wrote within a month, driving himself day and night, so badly did they need new plays. For this one he had gone back in English history to a time before the War of the Roses, to an earlier king, Richard II.

It was a daring subject to choose for a play, and if he had not been in such a hurry he might have given it more sober thought. In writing about the dethroning of a king, not by his natural heir but by another noble, Will was not attacking the theory of the divine right of kings; nor was he upholding the right of a stronger man to unseat a weaker one. He simply chose material that he thought would make an exciting story. But the play did contain dangerous lines that might lead an Englishman to wonder if a king or queen held his throne by divine right—especially when Richard II spoke such words as:

> . . . let us sit upon the ground,
> And tell sad stories of the death of kings:
> How some have been depos'd, some slain in war;
> Some haunted by the ghosts they have depos'd,
> Some poison'd by their wives, some sleeping kill'd:
> All murder'd . . .

Having become England's foremost dramatic writer, Will could be forgiven almost anything, and even Queen Elizabeth enjoyed the play. Perhaps, too, the fact that *Richard II* did not become one of the public's favorites helped; while it contained more poetry, more emotion, than *Richard III*, it attracted less attention. Excited audiences preferred—in fact, demanded—the scheming, violent, crookbacked Duke of Gloucester whose bloody deeds called forth their shouts and gestures of anger and hatred. Yet it was *Richard II* that was to cause Shakespeare trouble at some future date . . .

Will now shared in the profits of the company and was one of the managers. As he learned more about its business affairs, he found that he liked it—which he considered odd, remembering how he had hated all business matters in his father's glove shop.

In 1594 there were two rival acting companies: the Lord Chamberlain's Men and the Lord Admiral's Men. Ned Alleyn, aging and reluctantly continuing to appear in plays, had joined the Lord Admiral's group and was still the most popular figure on the London stage. Challenging his pre-eminence more and more was Richard Burbage, whose magnificent acting matched the dynamic roles he had in Will's plays. Before long the Theatre, where the Lord Chamberlain's Men played, began to draw in the crowds that once packed the Rose Theatre. Henslowe and Alleyn retaliated by hiring new writers as fast as they came along. Two and three would be put to work on the same play, to speed up the writing so a new play could be offered every few days.

With the production of *Romeo and Juliet* and A *Midsummer Night's Dream* Will Shakespeare finally attained fame and fortune. The fashionable world paid well for the honor of having his company play at private affairs and the public of London fought to get into the Theatre whenever his name appeared on the bills of advertisement.

Shakespeare's special genius was his deep understanding of human beings—their motivations, their needs, their weaknesses, their strengths. Coupled with this understanding was his masterful control of language, which permitted him to invest his characters with such true-to-life emotions that the audience could weep, laugh, hate, rejoice, suffer, with them—not just the first time but at every performance.

His love for his Dark Lady was poured into many of his sonnets, which he never expected to be published; nor were they until after both he and Anne were dead. He met this girl only a few times, then she drifted out of his life but not out of his heart and his plays.

Fortunately he was much too busy to dwell unhappily on his lost love. The Lord Chamberlain's Company brought together many actors, and Will found that, as one of the principal men of the company, there was much to be done: plays to be chosen or written, rehearsals and performances to be scheduled. Burbage, Kempe, Augustine Phillips and Will, as sharers, were soon joined by John Heminge, who proved to be the best businessman of them all.

The plot for Shakespeare's next play was forced upon him when a terrible scandal suddenly burst upon London. The Earl of Essex had uncovered a plot against the Queen's life! Her personal physician, the elderly Dr. Lopez, had accepted money from the King of Spain to poison Elizabeth, and had been caught just in time by Essex. After being tortured, Dr. Lopez broke down and confessed to the crime. On June 7 of 1594 he was taken to Tyburn where, in front of mocking crowds, he cried out that his confession had been a lie and that he dearly loved his Queen. In spite of his protest, he was hanged.

Essex was triumphant. Hadn't the Cecils tried to say Dr. Lopez was innocent? Hadn't he protected the Queen and, what was more important, proved that Philip of Spain was treacherous? Wasn't that enough reason to go to war?

The people of London were so stirred up by the affair that the Lord Chamberlain's Men were urged to perform something suitable to the mood of the times. Marlowe's *Jew of Malta* had been popular, and now Will was told to write a similar play, because Dr. Lopez had been a Jew.

The Merchant of Venice bore slight resemblance to Marlowe's plot, and Shakespeare's Shylock was entirely different from the Jew of Malta. Although not admirable, he was a sensitive, very human man.

In spite of the hysteria over the Lopez affair, in spite of the fact that Shakespeare was aware of the general prejudices of his time, he could not make the Jew in *The Merchant of Venice* a cheap or cruel villain, but merely a man whose own sufferings goaded him into seeking revenge.

There were very few Jews in England, for most of them had been banished many years before, with the exception of a few like Dr. Lopez. Even when Jews had lived there, they had not been permitted to own land or work in very many trades. They had existed as best they could, and the one profession open to them was money-lending, since the Church forbade any Christian to do this. Many people had to borrow money, but they despised the Jews who lent it to them.

No play that Shakespeare had written thus far had shown how complex human nature was and how the rules of society could twist even good people.

The merchant of Venice, Antonio, was upright, decent, respected by his friends, yet he spat on Shylock because he was a Jew and a money-lender. Shylock, lonely, unafraid, proud of his people, hating Antonio for the indignities he had inflicted, was so hurt that he could think of nothing but revenge. Life was not easy for a man who knew himself to be an outcast from society, tolerated only for the money he could lend.

Antonio borrowed a large sum from Shylock in order to help a friend who needed money to court the wealthy, beautiful Portia. Antonio was unable to return the money when the debt fell due, and Shylock made ready to claim the forfeit—a pound of Antonio's flesh. Portia, disguised as a young lawyer, argued the case brilliantly, seeming to agree with Shylock, but at the last moment warned him that the contract called for *flesh*: if one drop of Antonio's blood should be shed, Shylock would be liable to the charge of murder. Naturally Shylock could not carry out his revenge.

At first Shakespeare's play puzzled the Londoners, who had expected a villain they could despise, not a man who moved them to pity even in his hatred and desire for vengeance. When Shylock spoke the immortal lines:

> I am a Jew: hath not a Jew eyes? hath not a Jew hands, organs, dimensions, senses, affections, passions? fed with the same food, hurt with the same weapons, subject to the same diseases, healed by the same means, warmed and cooled by the same winter and summer, as a Christian is? If you prick us, do we not bleed? if you tickle us, do we not laugh? if you poison us, do we not die?

and if you wrong us, shall we not revenge?—if we are like you in the rest, we will resemble you in that. . . . The villainy you teach me, I will execute; and it shall go hard, but I will better the instruction . . .

the listeners felt uneasy and knew not why.

In a matter of a few short weeks, however, a new mood settled over London, and Shylock now had the genuine sympathy of the audiences. A rumor started, and spread all over the City, that the Earl of Essex had fabricated the charges against Dr. Lopez and that the old man had been completely innocent. Arguments flared up, duels and brawls were fought as some called Essex a murderer while others staunchly defended him.

No one felt worse than William Shakespeare. Once proud to be Essex's friend, now he was ashamed. "You have no doubts about the truth of this, do you, Florio?" he asked when his friend, very upset, came to see him.

"None," Florio answered decisively. "Of course, my lord the Earl of Southampton denies that Essex could have been so base, but I am convinced that he concocted the whole plot in an effort to discredit the Cecils, gain more influence with the Queen and perhaps win support for a war against Spain. We have both observed the impatience Essex has shown when he cannot have his own way." Then Florio added unhappily, "I have left Southampton's service. We parted in friendly fashion—but we have parted."

"I fear that things will never be the same again, Florio," Will replied.

Gradually the talk and the furor died down, but the Earl of Essex lost some of his popularity with the people as well as with his Queen. Though it was still said that he would succeed Elizabeth, who was growing old, it was not uttered with the same enthusiasm.

Richard Burbage had bad news of an entirely different kind for Will. Kempe had left the company. "I think, perhaps, it is because the Theatre is so old and run down. After all, it was the first one in London. Henslowe has spent hundred of pounds remodeling his Rose Theatre and now it attracts actors as well as the audience."

There was nothing that either of them could do about it. They wanted to build a new theatre of their own, but they remained with old James Burbage out of loyalty. One day they would be free to do as they pleased; in the meantime, profits were good and both Richard and Will were becoming modestly wealthy.

With his mind troubled about Southampton and Essex's headstrong actions, it was easier for Will to revive his old plays, act in them, busy himself with management, than it was for him to write. And so another year went by.

As 1596 opened, Will and Richard began to seriously consider building their own theatre and were trying to decide the best location for it. Suddenly tragic news arrived from Stratford. Hamnet, his son, was very ill.

Though Will rode as fast as horses could take him, he walked into the Henley Street house just as the boy was dying. Holding the child in his arms, he was filled with a grief that was almost unbearable.

The loss of his son made him understand the sorrow of death in a new, deeply personal way, and he was drawn closer to Anne as he comforted her and shared her burden of pain.

William Shakespeare had so well understood young, ardent love, jealousy, romance; now he became aware of the strength and the sorrows of old men and women as he saw his parents mourn and realized that they, too, had lost children. Through Anne he sensed what it meant to be a mother, bear children and lose them.

He had once thought his father foolish to want so much to have a coat of arms and regain the property of Asbies; now he saw that it was not for himself that John Shakespeare wanted these things but for his sons. The money Will had been saving to build a new theatre and improve the company, he spent to buy back Asbies. He also applied for the coat of arms and, because he had gained fame, it was quickly granted. While he was still in Stratford, Will had the satisfaction of putting this grant into his father's hands, but for himself it was meaningless—little Hamnet would never grow up to call himself a "gentleman."

To divert Anne's attention, he bought New Place, the old home of Sir Hugh Copton and the finest mansion in Stratford. He helped her to settle in, but then an urgent message recalled him to London.

While he had been away, other men had been making history. Spain had attempted to build a second Armada, but while it was still making ready in the port of Cadiz, Drake and Hawkins led an English fleet there. After the ships were sunk, the Earl of Essex and his men landed and took the town and surrounding hills by force.

This was what Essex had always wanted—an attack—even though the Cecils and Elizabeth had opposed such action. But the skirmish regained for Essex the popularity he once had with the people, despite the fact that it accomplished little and the English withdrew from Spanish soil immediately. Again Essex's name was on the lips of all Englishmen; his star was once more ascending.

The Lord Chamberlain, worried that Essex was growing too popular, too arrogant, too impatient for the throne, had sent for Shakespeare, and urged him to write a play on the theme of unhappy rebellion. Will, who had not forgotten that side of Essex which could be so ruthless, agreed to do so, but his personal grief was too recent to be pushed aside during the writing of *King John*. Although the play lacked the genius of his other historical dramas, it contained some beautiful speeches, particularly those Will wrote for the mother who grieved for her dead son. The words came from his own sorrowing heart:

> He talks to me that never had a son. . . .
> Grief fills the room up of my absent child,
> Lies in his bed, walks up and down with me,
> Puts on his pretty looks, repeats his words,

Remembers me of all his gracious parts,
Stuffs out his vacant garments with his form;
Then, have I reason to be fond of grief.

That winter Will appeared with his company at the Christmas Revels of the Queen, but in the summer of 1597 he returned to Stratford. New Place, with its beauty and the comfort of its spacious rooms, was a proud fulfillment in Will's life. It was the indisputable proof that John Shakespeare's dreaming son, the young man who had run away to London with actors, had come back as one of the town's richest and most prominent citizens.

He was particularly happy for Anne's sake, for he felt guilty that he had spent so little time with his family. He had taken no part in the raising of his two daughters and had had little opportunity to know his son, now gone forever. Anne had borne the entire burden of raising the children, teaching them, amusing them, sitting up with them when they were ill, watching over them day after day. He felt humble when he realized that she had never let the children forget him or stop loving him.

Though time and the loving warmth of his family helped him, it was work that would heal Will's grief, and he soon grew impatient to be back in London. He knew that laughter can be a remedy for sorrow, and so he wrote the first part of *Henry IV*, creating the wonderful, comic figure of Falstaff.

When *Henry IV* was played in London, the whole city went wild over that bawdy, ridiculous, fat old rogue. The people could not get enough of Falstaff, the butt of every joke but with the wit to turn the joke back on others. Soon everyone was talking about the rollicking companion of young Prince Hal, who would as soon play a trick on a prince as he would on any of his witless drinking companions. Falstaff, the coward; Falstaff, the ladies' man—how the audiences loved that monstrous tub of a fellow! At every performance they howled with laughter at him. When he left the stage they would stop the show with their cries for "Falstaff!"

After such a reception, the Lord Chamberlain's Men agreed

that Will should stop acting for a while and concentrate on writing a second part of the life of Henry IV so the audiences could have more of Falstaff. When the new play was almost finished, the plague threatened the City again and the company went on tour. Will went back to Stratford to finish the final scenes.

Old James Burbage had died in February of 1597. A month later the Lord Chamberlain also died, but his son was given his place of honor at court and he continued his father's patronage. Thus the company had not dissolved and was still known as the Lord Chamberlain's.

The plague did not strike London so severely that year, and Will returned to face the pressing problem of finding a theatre. After Burbage's death, the owners of the land on which the Theatre stood refused to renew the lease. The two Burbage sons, Richard and Cuthbert, owned the building but what good would it do them if they could not rent the land? The whole company met and came to a decision—they would build their own theatre, even though they did not have the money to do so.

"When I think of all that good lumber and material in the Theatre going to waste!" Richard stormed during the meeting. "The owners of the land are just going to tear it down."

One thought entered all their minds almost simultaneously. Startled by it, they looked at each other. Smiles came, and quick gleams in the eye, and finally they roared with laughter. They would do it!

14

The players told no one of their plans. They chose a site for their new theatre and Heminge bought the land on the other side of the Thames beyond the Bear Garden and Henslowe's Rose. Once the deed was signed, they gathered one very early morning to carry out their plot.

Grown men, all of them, they approached their task with the deviltry of twelve-year-olds. Before it was light they were hard at work tearing down the old theatre. Will and Richard and Cuthbert were strong men, but older ones like Pope and Heminge puffed and panted at their unaccustomed labors.

Passers-by stopped on their way to work to watch the actors swarming all over the big building, sawing, hammering, and chopping away at it. The landowners heard the racket and came running, screaming they would have the law on them. But there was nothing that anyone could do—the Theatre belonged to the Burbage brothers.

Every bit of precious wood and brick was loaded onto hired carts and hauled away to the new site, to be used for the theatre they had already named the Globe. Clouds of dust and dirt rolled over them, they were exhausted, their hands were blistered. But they were happy and proud of themselves.

"If you could see yourself, Will!" Richard burst into laughter. "The great William Shakespeare—the friend of earls, the man whose plays delight all of London—covered from head to foot with dust and wood shavings! Your face is smudged and filthy——"

"And yours is as begrimed and black as mine own!" Will retorted.

Late that evening a procession of men—each carrying a forgotten board, a pedestal or a few bricks—walked from Shoreditch down Bishopsgate Street, past Eastcheap. They crossed the Thames into Southward, made a right turn through the Liberty of the Clink and arrived at the large plot of ground where their theatre would one day stand. The Burbage brothers put in half the money needed to build it; Shakespeare, Phillips, Pope, Heminge and Kempe put in the rest. Now they would all be part owners, and as such would divide the profits as well as the money made from the sale of food and drink during performances.

While the Globe was being built, the company rented the Swan Theatre and put on a new Shakespeare play, *Much Ado About Nothing*. It did not rank with his better plays, but everyone enjoyed acting in the comedy. Two of the favorite characters were Beatrice and Benedick, who mocked and teased each other throughout the play. Will also introduced ordinary, everyday characters like Dogberry and Verges who stole the show every time they appeared onstage.

Shakespeare then decided that he had to do something about Falstaff. Unless he killed him, the public would demand no one else. So in his next play, *Henry V*, Falstaff died. The audience cried, but they were not too certain whether the old rogue had died of a broken heart or from drinking too much ale.

In the *Henry IV* plays, Falstaff had been the boon companion of devil-may-care Prince Hal; together they had roistered in taverns, played ridiculous jokes on each other. But when Hal became King Henry V, his wild days were over and he had to prove himself a monarch worthy of ruling his people. The adventures of Henry V swept the spectators into an exalted patriotic mood. Before the battle of Agincourt, the young king spoke to his men:

> We few, we happy few, we band of brothers;
> For he today that sheds his blood with me
> Shall be my brother; be he ne'er so base
> This day shall gentle his condition.

The audience went wild upon hearing those words. Though still held by the old idea that the nobility ruled and the people were meant only to serve, the first notions of equality were stirring in the hearts of Englishmen. If they shed their blood for England, were they not as brave as any noble at whose side they fought? Shakespeare had put into words something they dimly but deeply felt.

Will saw the Earl of Southampton twice that year but the encounters left them both unhappy. The warm friendship was gone. Southampton could speak of nothing but praise for Essex, defending his actions and expressing anger at the Queen for not yet naming Essex as her successor. Will's life suddenly seemed devoid of friendship—even Burbage was too wrapped up in the theatre to talk or think about anything else. But this emptiness was soon to be filled by a man unlike anyone Will had ever known before.

He had read a play called *Every Man in His Humour* by someone called Ben Jonson. "I think we should produce it," he told Burbage. "The author is one of Henslowe's writers, but at the moment he is out of favor and I think we could buy and produce the play ourselves."

Richard objected. "I know about Jonson—he's a trouble maker. He has just been imprisoned in Marshalsea because his *Isle of Dogs* is considered a treasonous play. Why risk offending the Lord Chamberlain by playing *Every Man in His Humour*?"

"Because it is excellent," Will answered. He was seldom insistent, but on the rare occasions that he was, Burbage knew there was no arguing with him.

Jonson came out of prison, only to go right back in again for dueling with one of Henslowe's players and killing him. Curious about a man who was so fine a writer and so constantly in trouble, Will went to Jonson's trial at the Old Bailey. He hated prisons and courtrooms, and the degradation of the poor wretches on trial distressed him. But the moment Ben Jonson was led into the prisoner's dock, Will forgot the unpleasant surroundings and everything else in his surprise.

It was not just the huge, bulky frame and the ugly face, it was the personality of the man that was so startling. Ben Jonson dominated the courtroom. He made fools of judge and lawyers. In spite of his swashbuckling airs and bravado, he clearly displayed his lightning wit, intelligence and education.

Will was delighted to hear Jonson's defense, and had to hide his face in his hands several times to keep from laughing out loud. The rascal was pleading the right of clergy—an outdated law which stated that any man who could read and write could not be tried by anything but a religious court. In times past, usually only members of the clergy were educated, and the old law had somehow survived. It was on this point that Ben Jonson won his freedom.

When he was released the next day Will was waiting for him in a nearby inn. He had been watching out the window and, as soon as he spied the burly figure step through the prison gates, he sent a messenger to bring him to his table. Jonson plunged into the room, looking about him with curiosity and arrogance. Will half rose from his bench and bowed to him.

Jonson came over and sat down. "You are Shakespeare? I think I now owe you two favors. Heminge told me that it was you who insisted on the Chamberlain's Men buying my play. If you are about to buy my breakfast, I am twice in your debt."

"We will celebrate your freedom." Will called out an order for food and drink.

"Freedom?" Jonson held out his thumb. "Look at that—they burned the brand of a felon on me, the dogs. Ah well, it was worth it. That scurvy rascal deserved to die and my dispatching him was an act of service to my country."

"How had he offended you?" Will asked.

"Why, the man pretended to have learning, whereas he had none. I who was educated at Westminster under the greatest teacher that ever lived, Master Camden, I know what learning is: I read and study every day of my life. It is a passion with me.

And when I see a fool like that preening himself in his ignorance —well, the world is well rid of him."

Never were two men more unalike than William Shakespeare and Ben Jonson, yet never were two more drawn to each other. That morning set the seal on their friendship. They spoke often of their work, for they shared the same passion for writing. They spoke of politics and Ben roared his wrath against Essex:

"Stirring up the country, making trouble, trying to make the Cecils lose favor with the Queen! Now he's off to Ireland. He finally persuaded Her Majesty to let him go there to put down some fool rebellion. What he really hopes is that Elizabeth will regret his absence so terribly she will call him back and give him anything he wants."

"I doubt that the Queen has felt the same toward him since the Lopez affair. She may not know the facts of the case—indeed, no one seems to—but I would venture that she suspects Essex of being guilty."

"And what of Southampton? Has he gone to Ireland too?" Jonson asked with his usual directness.

An expression of unhappiness crossed Will's face. "Yes. But before that he offended the Queen by marrying one of her Ladies in waiting without asking her permission. Bess put him in prison for a week to teach him a lesson—though I doubt he's learned it. I saw him once and tried to speak to him of his proper duty and loyalty, but, while I believe at heart he still respects my judgment, he would not listen."

Often the two men rowed far up the river Thames, out of sight and sound of the City, and now they were drifting slowly back toward London, past gentle green meadows.

Jonson leaned forward; the huge hand he placed on Shakespeare's shoulder was surprisingly gentle. "Be prudent, Will. Stay away from Southampton."

Will might not have heeded the advice, so deep was his affection for the young Earl, but Southampton and Essex were still in Ireland, doing nothing while Essex waited for the Queen to beg him to return. He had set out for Ireland in March of 1599, cheered by throngs of people in London and through every town, and his arrogance made him believe that he, not that stubborn old woman on the throne, was the favorite of all Englishmen.

He was furious that Elizabeth did not send for him, and he finally returned to London that autumn. In this mood he behaved so impudently and rudely to the Queen that, much as she loved him, she had him committed to the custody of Lord Keeper Egerton at York House in the Strand. Southampton was enraged, and suddenly became too busy seeing all sorts of mysterious visitors, making all sorts of secret plans, to see any of his old friends—including Will.

Meanwhile the building of the Globe went on slowly but steadily. A brief outbreak of the plague had put a stop to it for several months, and money was scarce. But the company was determined that it would be as perfect as they could make it, and preferred to wait rather than pinch pennies.

They had two tremendous successes during the winter of 1599 and the spring of 1600. Popular demand forced Shakespeare to write another play with Falstaff in it and he turned out that lusty, bawdy comedy, *Merry Wives of Windsor*. It was the hilarious account of the old rogue's efforts to court two very respectable women at the same time. Audiences were regaled by the capers and tricks that everybody played on everybody—and they especially loved it when the two clever women turned the tables on rascally old Falstaff.

Shakespeare felt happier than he had been for a long time. With Essex in prison, Southampton was free from his evil influence. The years had lessened the grief over Hamnet's death. Ben Jonson's cheering, stimulating companionship helped Will regain his good spirits. So he stopped acting and shut himself up in his rooms and began his new play, *As You Like It*.

The word spread that Shakespeare was hard at work on another play and was not to be disturbed. For a while he was not to be found sitting in THE MERMAID or taking a walk through the streets of London or rowing on the river. The two rooms he now lived in were comfortable, but even if they had not been, it would not have mattered. In spirit, Shakespeare was far away. He deliberately turned his back on all the troubles and problems in London and returned to the magic world of his boyhood—the Forest of Arden.

Rosalind and Celia wander through that forest looking for Rosalind's father, the real Duke, whose kingdom has been usurped by Celia's father, Duke Frederick. Orlando is also wandering the forest trying to escape death at the hand of his older brother Oliver. He hopes to find the Duke and join his band of exiles. He has fallen in love with Rosalind, whom he has seen just once, and everywhere he goes in the forest he pins love-songs to her on trees, which Rosalind finds.

Rosalind, disguised as a boy, is embarrassed to reveal herself to Orlando, but she thinks of ways to see him often, hear his love-songs to herself, and keep from revealing her true identity.

One day Orlando saves his brother from death by a lioness and Oliver repents. Rosalind reveals her true self and she and Orlando are happy. Celia and Oliver fall in love and are happy. The wicked Duke Frederick meets a religious hermit and is reformed; the real duke has his kingdom back—and all are happy.

When the play was produced the people of London took it to their hearts in the same spirit in which it was created. They went about the streets humming its songs; if a girl was saucy she was a "Rosalind"; if she was sweet she was a "Celia." The magic Forest of Arden had cast a spell over them too. The nonsense and beauty of the play reached out beyond the stage and touched their lives—as it had touched Shakespeare's. It was as if something had unconsciously whispered to him that never again would his heart sing this way, that darkness and unhappiness lay ahead of him. As You Like It was the peak of noonday and brightness, his last hopeful yearning that the world could be magic instead of what it was.

15

For the grand opening of the Globe Theatre in the autumn of 1600, Will wrote another historical drama, but this was set in ancient Rome rather than England.

It was noon of a crisp, cool day. Woodsmoke from the midday dinners curled from the chimneys in all the lanes and alleys as Shakespeare made his way to the enormous round, turreted building that was the Globe. As usual, when there was to be a first performance of one of his plays, he was nervous and he walked quickly. Today he was even more nervous than usual because this would also be the first play at the new theatre. Had everything been done? Had Heminge found a good doorkeeper? Had the Roman togas arrived, clean and fresh, for the players?

Suddenly he saw a handbill nailed to a post and he forgot all his worries as he stopped to read it:

The Tragedy of Julius Caesar. Underneath that was: *How Caesar Is Assassinated. The Conspiracy of Brutus. How Antony Stirs the Populace into Rebellion.* Below this was his name: *William Shakespeare.* Then: *Richard Burbage as Brutus.* And the time: *Three O'Clock.* The place. *The Globe Theatre.*

He felt a tightening in his throat. This was the day so long worked for and dreamed about. He stood before the Globe and looked up at the tall turret where a pennant fluttered in the breeze. The figure of Hercules holding a globe on his shoulders decorated the flag.

Quickening his steps, Will went around to a side door that opened into the center of the building, and entered. There were no seats downstairs. Here the "groundlings" would stand packed together, the front rows jammed up against the stage.

The building was open to the sky, and sunlight poured through the top, bringing every object into sharp focus, glistening on the new green and gilt and white paint of the low balcony railings. Stairs led to the three tiers of galleries, which contained seats and benches for those who could afford a shilling to sit and enjoy the plays in comfort.

Will critically examined the stage, which was like a square apron coming out into the circle of the yard, with a wide space on each side of it where spectators could stand. It stood on a foundation four feet high and Will had to look up to examine the pillars that supported the narrow overhang, called a "shadow," at the rear of the stage. It would serve several purposes during a play—an inside room in a house, a balcony . . . Was the overhang solid enough? Will shrugged. It was too late to worry about that now.

Stagehands came out carrying furniture, and he called to them: "You there, by the pillar. That bench will not be needed until the garden scene. Just place the statue of Caesar in the center—that's right."

He swung himself lithely up onto the stage, walked to the back where there was a curtained alcove. He noted with approval that the entrance doors on the right and left were large enough to permit a group of actors to burst through when such action was called for in a play. Then he heard his name being called and went backstage to the dressing room.

Richard Burbage, growing more handsome with the passing years, was standing there, dressed in a white Roman toga. There was a frown on his face.

"What is it, Richard? Surely you aren't worried that the public won't like the Globe?" Will fought down his own nervousness and made himself smile.

"No, I'm thinking about Brutus. Tell me again," Richard asked, "is he sincerely fond of Caesar? Or is he ambitious himself?"

145

"Brutus would not pretend an emotion he does not feel. You must play him like that, Richard."

They had been through this already, but Burbage always worried and fretted before a first performance. Will smiled at him again reassuringly and looked about at the other players who were dressing, applying make-up, reciting their lines, encouraging one another.

Young Robert Armin paused in the act of darkening his eyebrows to look up at Shakespeare. "Will," he said, "this role of Antony is the best you have given me. When I was a child actor you used to tell me that someday I would have parts like this. In the last year I've done mostly comedy. This is the best," he repeated merrily, "and I am going to steal the show from Richard!"

Armin's confidence lifted his own and Will relaxed somewhat. He hung his doublet on a nail, slipped off the wide neck ruff. Yes, the toga *was* clean and fresh from the washerwoman, and as he put it on he reproached himself for worrying about small matters when the play was the thing.

Over in one corner Henry Condell was repeating to himself: " 'O Cassius, if you could but win the noble Brutus to our party.' " He changed the pitch of his voice: " 'O Cassius, if you could but win——' " He lowered it an octave: " 'O Cassius, if you could——' "

"O Condell, if you could but be silent!" Pope yelled at him.

The men all laughed. A stranger entering the dressing room might have thought these restless, nervous players were unprepared for the performance, unsure of themselves. And so they were—until they stepped out on the stage. Then their fears abruptly left them; they were in complete control of their parts; everything they had learned in rehearsals came back to them promptly and easily.

As it neared three o'clock, the shuffle of feet and the muted sound of voices began to drift backstage through the heavy curtain. The noise grew louder as the first trickle of customers increased to a steady, surging flow of people trampling the rushes in the yard and clattering up the steps to the balconies. Now the high, shrill voices of the vendors could be heard as they started to move among the crowd, selling their wares:

"Buy a ripe, a pretty, a red apple!" . . . "Here, the best ale! Gentlemen, slake your thirst!" . . . "Cherries, cherries! Who'll buy cherries? A penny a poke!"

Two minutes to three . . . A blast of a trumpet from the turret startled the actors. Two more blasts and the play must begin. They all made hurried, last-minute adjustments to their costumes and their make-up.

As the third and last trumpet call rang out, a sudden stillness fell over the entire theatre as if every voice had been cut off in mid-air and every foot stopped in its tracks. Heminge walked out to announce the play and tell the audience the first scene was a street in Rome. Will nodded to the five actors who played the roles of ordinary citizens and they quickly walked out as Heminge came back. A burst of clapping greeted their entrance, then the people settled down to enjoy the play.

The five Roman citizens were draping wreaths around a statue of Julius Caesar, who was their hero. There was to be a great public festival that afternoon. Two tribunes approached and berated the men for their idolatry: there must be no more crowning of Caesar's images. He was neither king nor god.

Accompanied by his wife Calpurnia, and by Antony, Brutus, Cassius and others, Julius Caesar appeared, head held proudly high, regal and forceful in his bearing. As they crossed the public square, an ominous interruption halted their procession. An old soothsayer warned Caesar: "Beware the Ides of March!"

Caesar shrugged off the warning and swept on through the arch, but Brutus and Cassius lingered behind to speak.

Although the great and versatile general had won the respect and admiration of many Romans, he had also made bitter enemies; his dictatorial powers gave rise to fears and jealousies among his followers. Brutus was not certain whether his loyalties lay with the consul or the republic.

When Caesar passed by again and noted the two men talking

alone, he realized that deep and hidden resentments foster conspiracies and he said to Antony, "Let me have men about me that are fat, sleek-headed men, and such as sleep o'nights; yon Cassius has a lean and hungry look; he thinks too much: such men are dangerous."

Even though Brutus and Cassius learned that three times had Caesar been offered a crown and three times refused it, they suspected his intentions. Might he not be pretending, rejecting kingship but secretly determined to have it in his own good time?

A group of conspirators met in Brutus' garden late at night to determine their course of action. When the men slipped silently away, to return to their beds, the fate of Caesar was sealed. For the good of all Rome, he must die.

Caesar's wife, awakened by fearsome dreams, begged her husband not to go to the Senate that day, lest evil befall. Caesar himself hesitated, recalling the soothsayer's words, but when one of the plotters came to fetch the consul and taunted him: "Lo, Caesar is afraid?" it was a challenge no man could ignore.

So tense was the atmosphere, so real the passions, that the spectators no longer were in London. They stood outside the Roman Senate, pressed closer as Caesar approached the inner house where the conspirators concealed themselves in the shadows. The audience waited breathlessly as Caesar spoke to the soothsayer: "The Ides of March are come," and heard the portentous reply: "Ay, Caesar, but not gone." Would this Roman consul heed the second warning? Everyone in the theatre knew that he could not.

Surrounded by the men whom he had lifted to power and glory, Caesar died as their hands plunged daggers into his body, addressing his last words to the friend who betrayed him: "Et tu, Brute? Then fall, Caesar."

The people closest to the stage were in a turmoil of emotions, as if they themselves had clutched the weapons that inflicted those mortal wounds. Englishmen had become Romans and were horrified at the bloody deed they had just witnessed. It was only when Marc Antony rushed onstage that they quieted down to watch what would happen next. Another murder? But no, Antony's life was spared, and it was agreed that he would deliver the funeral oration.

Brutus addressed the huge Roman crowd that gathered, speaking so calmly and reasonably that for a while the people seemed to accept his word that Caesar had to die if Romans were to remain free. Then Antony spoke:

> He was my friend, faithful and just to me:
> But Brutus says, he was ambitious;
> And Brutus is an honourable man . . .
> When that the poor have cried, Caesar hath wept;
> Ambition should be made of sterner stuff;
> Yet Brutus says, he was ambitious;
> And Brutus is an honourable man . . .
> I thrice presented him a kingly crown,
> Which he did thrice refuse. Was this ambition?
> Yet Brutus says, he was ambitious:
> And, sure, he is an honourable man . . .

As Antony spoke those words, his tone sharpened to bitter sarcasm. He knew Brutus was truly honorable; that Brutus had killed only because he believed Caesar to be a threat to liberty and freedom. Antony's sarcasm twisted this honorable reputation to make the people believe that Brutus was a lying traitor.

Antony's sarcasm did its work. It stung as a whip, inflaming his audience to a fury that drove the conspirators out of Rome. But Antony knew that they would return with armies and he was right. Brutus and Cassius came back prepared for battle, and Antony's army was hard pressed to hold them back. Finally Cassius was forced to retreat and, believing that Brutus, too, was losing, ordered a friend to slay him. With his death, the tide that had been with Brutus suddenly turned against him and he lost more and more ground until he found himself alone, deserted except for a few faithful companions. He pleaded with them to kill him, to spare him the disgrace of being taken captive by

Antony. But they were too devoted to him to do so, and finally he fell upon his own sword and died.

Antony, looking down upon his body, felt little satisfaction in victory. Of his now-dead enemy he said, "This was the noblest Roman of them all." Brutus *was* an honorable man.

For a long moment after the play ended there was a breathless hush all through the Globe. Three thousand people screamed and cheered and applauded. Those on the ground surged up toward the stage to rush upon the actors.

It was a tremendous tribute but it could lead to destruction. The dead Brutus quickly jumped to his feet and became the live Richard Burbage. With hands outstretched, he tried to stop the mob.

"Gentle people, citizens, friends . . ." His words checked the forward movement. In a ringing voice that reached every person, even those still yelling, he cried, "The play is over!"

The cheers began again but the people moved back and slowly, reluctantly, headed for the exits, still talking excitedly and cheering the players and the author, until at last the Globe stood silent and deserted.

That Christmas of 1600 Queen Elizabeth chose more plays from the Lord Chamberlain's Men than she did from the Lord Admiral's. Henslowe had built a new Fortune Theatre, which was even more splendid than the Globe, but neither Shakespeare nor Burbage worried about it because their company was more popular with both the Queen and the people of London.

For the Christmas Revels William Shakespeare had a new comedy, *Twelfth Night*. While it pleased Elizabeth and proved to be a success later at the Globe, it was not a gay, sweet comedy, as his earlier ones had been. There was a slightly bitter tinge to it, more sarcasm and less sauciness. The wit was delicate and to the point, but the heroine Viola was not as marvelous a creation as Rosalind and Sir Toby Belch could not compare with Falstaff.

Will was hardly in the mood to write comedies, being so worried over Southampton and Essex, who had been released. What was going to happen to them? He had seen his patron several times in the past year, but the meetings had only served to distress Shakespeare further—the Earl, more under Essex's influence than ever, had changed a great deal and refused to discuss anything with Will.

Appropriately enough, *Twelfth Night* was given at Whitehall on the Twelfth Night after Christmas. The performance was held in the banqueting room and the actors had to use the center of the room without any raised stage. From this position they were closer to the throne and Will was able to observe Queen Elizabeth more closely. He could not help but notice how tired and careworn she looked. He was grateful that the play made her laugh. The only thing he remembered about that occasion was not the elaborately decorated hall and the bejeweled court members but the fragile, aging Queen, sitting proudly upright, yet so burdened, lonely and anxious.

Fear of her death and fear for the fate of the country hung like a brooding cloud over England. Some people murmured, "Why not Essex named successor?" "No, not Essex," others replied. "Remember Dr. Lopez?" But if not Essex, who then? Surely not James of Scotland, son of the dead Mary Stuart and rumored to be a very unpleasant man!

In February of 1601 Shakespeare received a message from the Earl of Southampton, asking him to call. When Will arrived at Drury House, it was not the same Southampton who had once greeted him so warmly and had been so pleased with *Venus and Adonis*. Now he sat in the same room, brooding and thoughtful, hardly raising his head when Will spoke to him.

"I have a favor to ask," he said abruptly.

"You have done many for me, my lord. Whatever you ask, it will be a pleasure to oblige." Any debt that Shakespeare owed Southampton had been well repaid by the honor the young nobleman had received as patron of the foremost poet and dramatist—but Will was remembering their friendship.

The Earl's sigh was a mixture of relief and embarrassment.

He rose to his feet, seeming to shake off his former mood and become resolute. His tone of voice was now hard:

"It's a small thing, actually . . . I would have your company play *Richard II* on the Saturday afternoon of the seventh of this month. Will you promise me this?"

Will thought the request strange and puzzling, since the play had never been one of Southampton's particular favorites. But, in truth, it was a small favor—one that there was no reason to refuse. "Certainly, my lord, if you wish it so."

"I do wish. And it will be Saturday, without fail?"

Will bowed. "The seventh." Then he added, "We are playing *Twelfth Night* again on the third. Have you seen it? Would you like me to reserve a place for you?"

"On the third? No. Some friends are meeting—are coming here on a matter of great importance. I am sorry but I will not be free that afternoon."

Shakespeare bowed again and turned to leave but on a sudden, swift impulse Southampton walked up to him and placed his arm on Will's shoulder. For one moment he looked happy again, and openhearted. "Ah, Will, how I wish things could have been different! I wish we could all go back to what we were. Do you remember that night when Burbage read *Venus and Adonis*? You and I thought then that life would always be as wonderful as it was that night, with no troubles besetting us and the future serene. Well—no matter. Good-by, my friend."

Burbage and the other players grumbled a bit at having to do *Richard II* on Saturday. Another play had been scheduled then and this was a change of plans. But it was never wise to refuse the Earl a request. When Saturday came, they performed *Richard II*, the story of how easy it was, how sometimes necessary it was, to dethrone one monarch and put another on the throne.

The next morning, Sunday the 8th, Will awoke to the sounds of bells ringing an alarm. Outside his window he heard a man running down the street, yelling something unintelligible. Shakespeare dressed hurriedly and went downstairs to speak to his landlord, Christopher Montjoy:

"What is it? Why are the bells ringing?"

"I don't know, sir. There's a lot of noise coming across the river and I've seen what seemed to be hundreds of mounted men and heard their trumpets—if I didn't know better, I would say it was war. But what would war trumpets be doing in London? Can it be the Spaniards?"

Will had no idea, but he hurried down to the river to cross the Thames, anxious to reach the City. At the wharf there were fewer boats and boatmen than usual, and those who were there looked frightened. "Come!" he called. "Here's a fare. I want to go across."

"Master Shakespeare, sir"—one took his money hesitatingly— "if you insist, I will ferry you across, but all the river traffic to-day is coming this way. People want to get out of London. They say it is an uprising. All kinds of rumors are floating about—but one thing is sure: it is the Earl of Essex's doings."

When they reached the other side, Will climbed out of the boat and ran up the river stairs. He saw people crowding the upper-story windows of the houses, peering out of doorways, huddling in two's and three's in the narrow street. Everyone was whispering and gesturing. The noise of mounted men was drawing nearer, and Will could hear the martial blasts of a bugle.

"It's the Earl! It's Essex!" A man came racing along the street. "He's riding into the City with hundreds of men and calling on everybody to follow him—he says he's going to tumble the Queen off her throne!" The man ran off to bawl his news down the other streets.

The drumming of horses' hoofs was coming closer; Will thought he could even hear shouts. The people on the street were slowly moving. He watched fearfully, wondering, would they rally around Essex? He was their gallant, daring leader. These men of London had only to rush inside, seize whatever weapons they had and join the Earl.

But in the doorway of the woodworker's shop, the owner sighed deeply and turned away. He put his arms around his weeping wife and they went in and closed the door behind them.

153

Overhead, windows were being shuttered and barred. People began to hasten to their homes and lock themselves in. They loved Essex, but the Queen was the Queen. Bess had a place in their hearts that no one could usurp.

Will stepped into an inn nearby and found a place for himself in an alcove, where he could look out the windows. The innkeeper stood at his elbow; both men were tense. They saw the mounted men coming, filling the streets, crying yells of rebellion. Essex was at their head but Will was looking for someone else— and soon found him: Southampton was riding at the Earl's side. He had thrown in his lot with treason.

By evening it was all over. The people of London had not followed Essex and his little troop. There had been one skirmish with the Queen's soldiers at Lud Gate, but Essex's men lost heart when they saw that they stood alone. The great uprising proved to be only a small rebellion. Essex surrendered, and with him Southampton.

The afternoon performance at the Globe was canceled—an audience would hardly be expected on such a day. The actors gathered backstage at the request of the Lord Chamberlain, but Will Shakespeare was not among them. Burbage went in search of him and found him in his lodgings, sitting in the dark in front of his window.

"All alone, Will, and not even one candle lit?"

There was no answer. Richard lighted a candle and held it up, and when the flickering flame outlined the heartbreak and despair on his friend's face, he was alarmed. "You're ill! I'll fetch a physician."

"There is no physician who can cure my ailment, Richard. The time is out of joint; there is a curse on all of us. We have believed too long that life was good and would serenely grow better . . . But it is not so! As flies to wanton boys, are we to the gods; they kill us for their sport," he said bleakly.

Was this the man who had captured joyous song and magic beauty in his plays as no one else ever had? Burbage's heart misgave him. "Because some men are fools, Will, must you——"

"Fools? They are human beings. Essex was brave and clever; Southampton, loyal and good. But we are all men; in our own natures, frail. A part of Essex's nature was ambition, and part of Southampton's was pride. How did these grow to such monstrous proportions? We are tricked in our own natures. How much of what we do is our own responsibility and how much of it is chance, fate, the actions of others?"

"Will, you have always seen the good and the bad in mankind," Richard pointed out, seeking desperately for a way to comfort his friend.

"Aye, the people of London whose hearts once went out to Essex in adulation—those same people will gather, with ugly curiosity, to watch their idol bend his neck to the chopping block. For beheaded he must be. You know that. The Queen must kill the traitor she loves." Will's voice broke with the horror of it. "What makes men cruel, blind, revengeful, disloyal, selfish? When I remember Southampton's kindness and friendship to me, do you wonder that I am sick at the thought of what may happen to him now?"

Richard Burbage moved nearer to his friend, but did not look at him as he spoke: "There is even worse to tell you, Will. The Lord Chamberlain told us this afternoon that we are in serious trouble. We are suspected of complicity in this rebellion. Southampton played traitor to you, Will. He asked that you perform *Richard II* hoping to prepare people for the deposing of the Queen and stirring them up in Essex's behalf."

Shakespeare got up from his chair and stumbled to the window. "Oh, monstrous treachery! Can this be so?" he cried out in agony. "I am sick of this false world!" He stared down at the street and saw, not the lively, gay London he loved, but the filth and the mud, the beggary of the poor, the meanness and greed.

Perhaps Burbage could shrug his shoulders and accept the world and men as he found them—but not so Shakespeare. His sensitive, poetic nature was both a blessing and a curse. It had permitted him to create great plays, but it had also shielded him from the harsh realities of life. He had written about the evil that men could do; he was aware of the vices that beset mankind —but he had never been personally touched by the perfidy of which man is capable. In his disillusionment and hurt, he kept asking himself how it was possible for good, honest, noble men to give way to such ugly passions as disloyalty, treason. That he could find no answer added further to his torment.

Nine days later Augustine Phillips was called before the Attorney-General to make his deposition in the matter of the performance of *Richard II*. The Attorney-General obviously believed that some members of the company were in the plot to help Southampton. This was a grave charge which could mean death for those found guilty. Eventually, through the intercession of the Lord Chamberlain and the sincerity of Shakespeare's own account of what had happened, the Attorney-General finally judged him to be innocent and the charges were dropped.

Southampton was sentenced to life imprisonment but on the 25th of February, 1601, the Earl of Essex was beheaded. The Queen and all of England sorrowed, and a shadow seemed to fall over the land.

16

William Shakespeare attempted to bury his sorrow in work on a new play, but more grief came to him when his father died on September 8 of that same year. For once Stratford had no cure for Will's troubled soul. He now found himself the head of the family. His sister Joan had married Will Hart, a hatter by trade, and their first child was one year old. Gilbert had taken over his father's business and Richard and Edmund helped him, although Edmund wanted to become an actor in London. Anne and the children were happy in New Place. In order to ensure his family's future, Will invested some of the money the Globe brought him in Stratford property. He bought one hundred thirty acres of farming land on the outskirts of town; the rents from it would add to the Shakespeare income.

When Will went to London at Christmastime for the Queen's Revels, Edmund went with him. There was no difficulty in getting his brother work as an actor, but his presence in the city did not help lighten Will's mood. There was too much difference in age and experience to establish a close relationship.

The Lord Chamberlain's Men and the Lord Admiral's Company had a new rival in the Lord Worcester's Men, and Shakespeare was asked to write more plays for the Globe. Now thirty-eight years old, famous, respected, well to do, Will knew what his public wanted: more Falstaffs and magic forests, more fairylands and tender love stories, more tense, exciting tales of England's history. But he could not write these plays. It was the human soul and spirit that absorbed him now. He was melancholy, filled with the sense of tragedy, horrified by the forces that drove men to their own destruction.

His next play was *The Tragedy of Hamlet, Prince of Denmark.* It was a story about a young prince enjoying his university days until he received word that his beloved father had died and his uncle had married his mother, making him King of Denmark.

The sensitive Hamlet, more of a philosopher than a man of action, mourned deeply for his father and darkly brooded over his mother's marriage to a man he despised and distrusted. Even his love for Ophelia, daughter of the Lord Chamberlain Polonius, was poisoned by these events.

One night on the castle battlements the ghost of the late king appeared to Hamlet and told him that he had been murdered by the man who now wore the crown. The son promised to seek revenge for the death of his father, and the ghost departed. Hamlet was plunged into further indecision and despair. Was the ghost merely a creation of his own sick mind? If so, he must try to forget his promise. If not, he must kill his uncle. But how could he be sure what was truth and what was fantasy? When a strolling band of players came to the castle, Hamlet conceived of a way to find out. He would have them present a play enacting the murder of a king according to the facts revealed to him by the ghost. Watching his uncle closely during the performance, Hamlet saw him start, rise from his seat and order the actors to stop the play.

Now certain of his uncle's guilt, Hamlet's conflict became a torment to him—to act or not to act:

> To be, or not to be: that is the question:
> Whether 'tis nobler in the mind to suffer
> The slings and arrows of outrageous fortune,
> Or to take arms against a sea of troubles,
> And by opposing end them. To die: to sleep;
> No more; and by a sleep to say we end
> The heart-ache, and the thousand natural shocks
> That flesh is heir to . . .

His chance to kill the uncle came—but Hamlet could not bring himself to do it. He went instead to his mother whom he loved and despised. He upbraided her and in his anguish said to her: "You are the queen, your husband's brother's wife; and—would it were not so!—you are my mother." Suddenly, he heard a noise behind a curtain. In a flash all his indecision left him and he whipped out his sword and plunged it into the curtain. But it was not the wicked king, only poor, stupid Polonius who lay dead at his feet—poor Polonius who had come to take counsel with the queen and had hidden when Hamlet came in.

Ophelia who had been hurt by Hamlet's strange, wild moodiness and the cruel things he had said to her, went mad over her father's death and drowned herself. Her brother Laertes challenged Hamlet to a duel for sport; the wicked king plotted with Laertes to poison Hamlet with a cup of wine and, if this failed, Hamlet would die by the poison placed on the tip of Laertes' sword.

The duel took place. Hamlet was pierced by the poisoned sword but Laertes dropped it, Hamlet picked it up and wounded Laertes with his own sword. The queen drank the wine intended for Hamlet. Laertes, dying, confessed that he and the king had poisoned the sword; Hamlet, dying, finally killed the wicked king.

Shakespeare wrote into this play some of his own terrible conviction that a man's weakness could be a crime and be responsible for great harm to others. Yet that same weakness, in another time and place and situation, would be called goodness, sensitivity, idealism, a reluctance to indulge in savage revenge.

Hamlet was a man tortured, as was Shakespeare himself.

The London audience at first did not know what to make of this new Shakespeare. *Hamlet* was not what they expected of him, but once over the shock, they responded well to the play.

Shakespeare next wrote *Troilus and Cressida*, another historical tragedy, followed by *All's Well That Ends Well*. His company had begged him for something not quite so bitter, and *All's Well* ended well—but there was nothing light or gay about the story. *Measure for Measure*, which came next, was much the same and exhibited the genius that made Shakespeare the leading playwright of his time, regardless of whether the endings were happy or tragic.

Will did little acting while he was writing these plays, seeming to shun the company of others. He continued to display his customary gentle courtesy toward the Fields, Jonson, Burbage and the players, and managed to keep his melancholy fairly well concealed. But Burbage and Jonson knew that something was troubling him deeply.

At times Jonson had the knack of being able to rouse his friend out of his low spirit, and could even evoke a smile or a laugh. "These plays of yours are ridiculous," he would say. "Within two hours your hero may begin as a babe, grow to maturity and die of old age. Is this reality? I write with the unity of time and place. How can you expect an audience to skip fifty years with you and go from a garden in one scene to a battlefield in the next one?"

Will's reply was mild. "You do our audiences an injustice. In their mind's eye they can see a forest when there is not a tree on stage; a duel between four men becomes a battle between armies. Their imaginations soar as high and wide as do ours."

"Audience! Scum!" snorted Ben. "They are as uneducated as you are yourself, and you have little learning."

Will smiled for the first time at Jonson's argumentative words, but he refused to quarrel with his friend. They were sitting in THE MERMAID, where Jonson now held court. Around him flocked the new, young writers Henslowe hired: Thomas Dekker, John Fletcher, Francis Beaumont. When Fletcher and Dekker came in, Will got up and took his leave; he was not happy in company.

After his departure young Fletcher said, "I think, Ben, that, despite the way you speak to Will Shakespeare and your surly remarks to him, you are actually fond of him?"

Jonson exploded. "Fond of him? I love him to the point of idolatry. Is there a man alive in all the world who can write as he does? So fertile is his brain that he can afford to toss lines of immense power and beauty to his minor characters. Fond of him!"

Will began working on a new play, *Othello*, for the Christmas Revels of 1602, but the annual festivities were canceled. Queen Elizabeth was dying. She rallied slowly and with her last strength demanded that her Lord Chamberlain provide her a play on January 21.

Hamlet was certainly a somber choice, but if the Queen's body was frail her mind was not, and she was in no mood for sheer nonsense. Only a few of her Court were with her; too many people sapped her little strength. She could not sit but lay on cushions in her smaller Presence Chamber and never took her eyes off the players.

As the drama unfolded and the players acted scene after scene, Will wondered if such a story would disturb the sick Queen. When Hamlet spoke of his father:

> He was a man, take him for all in all,
> I shall not look upon his like again

did she perhaps think of her much-beloved Essex?

But he saw that she was leaning forward slightly and a little color had come into her cheeks; the plot held her and made her forget herself. Her brilliant mind still craved challenges; human passions, problems and philosophy were still as necessary to her as the air she breathed. She had little time left for the trivialities of life.

The play ended. There was silence in the room. The courtiers were too moved by the tragedy to applaud, even had the Queen permitted the noise.

In the next room Shakespeare was removing the false beard he had worn as Polonius when the Lord Chamberlain entered and beckoned to him. He hurriedly wiped his face, then, with heart beating fast, returned to the Queen's chamber and was led up to the cushioned throne-bed.

Elizabeth could say nothing, though she tried. There was no

strength in her for speech, but her eyes, looking into his, thanked him, and one tiny, withered hand was held out to him. Kneeling, he pressed it to his lips. There was a touch on his shoulder and he rose to his feet and bowed out of the room.

On March 24, 1603, Good Queen Bess died.

With her death there passed an age of unified vitality in the country. Holding firmly the reins of government, Elizabeth brought her people peace and prosperity, had encouraged trade instead of warfare, had stimulated a robust interest in literature, drama and music. She left a strong, rich country to James of Scotland, who now came to the English throne and was crowned James I at Westminster Abbey on July 25, 1603.

Not only was England in mourning for a queen they had deeply loved, and reluctant to accept this newcomer—the whole nation began to stir in unrest as different groups, which Elizabeth had held in firm check, started to clamor for their presumptive rights. The Puritans wanted more rigid laws against theatres, dancing and other amusements; the Catholics hoped for more freedom under the son of Catholic Mary; the Anglican clergymen were determined that there should be but one English Church. More and more the younger sons of the nobility, reading the handwriting on the wall, were investing in shipping and trade, so that now businessmen wanted more of a voice in Parliament.

Such unrest could become ugly and under James it did, for he could satisfy no one. Wanting total power and authority in his own hands, he nevertheless imagined himself an enlightened and benevolent ruler. He was convinced that he knew what was best for England, and expected to be loved for his tyranny. But he never understood the English people and, worse, he underestimated them.

One of his first acts was to issue letters-patent making the Lord Chamberlain's Men his own servants. They became known as the King's Players and, as such, were to enjoy a favored position they had never had under Elizabeth. But when the members of the company were formally introduced to King James and

Queen Anne in an impressive ceremony, Will's heart was heavy. Was this a figure of majesty—this king who spoke with a slobber, whose extravagant clothes could not hide his thin, weak legs and whose compliments to Shakespeare, the writer, and to the company as actors, were really compliments to himself for having chosen them? Was this monarch, with his petty, narrow, conceited mind, to take the place of Elizabeth? Queen Anne was warmhearted, but silly and vain.

The royal couple wanted gaiety and pleasure: Will gave them the heart-rending story of *Othello*—and made them like it because James fancied himself a critic of drama. It was doubtful that the King truly understood the subtlety of the plot. It seemed merely a story of jealousy, but it was more than that.

Shakespeare knew something of the history of the Moors, those dark-skinned people of Moslem faith who had brought a wealth of culture, learning, science and architecture across the Mediterranean to the less advanced white people of southern Europe. Moorish power and culture declined with the passage of centuries, and their religion and dark skins had created a prejudice against them which still existed in the seventeenth century. Shakespeare's mind had soared above prejudice and intolerance. He was far more concerned with those forces in a human being that drive him to the desperation of murder. He chose to make his principal character a Moor because his motivations would be more complex.

Othello was a general of such courage and skill that the white men of Venice employed him and the majority of them respected him, knowing him to be distinguished, intelligent and good, a natural leader. Their troops willingly followed him, except for the villainous Iago, who hated him even as he pretended to be loyal.

The lovely Desdemona, daughter of a prominent Venetian, fell in love with Othello and he with her. Her father objected, but when the Venetian Duke heard her express, modestly, sweetly, yet sincerely, her love for the Moor, there was nothing to be done but accept their marriage.

Iago's main ambition was to bring about his downfall because Othello had made another man, Cassius, his chief lieutenant, and because he hated black skin. Othello, Iago, Cassius and the troops sailed to Cyprus to repel a large Turkish fleet, and Desdemona insisted on accompanying her husband.

When a severe storm wrecked the Turkish fleet, there was no war and Othello was appointed military commander of Cyprus. Iago was then in a position to put his schemes into action. He planted a seed of distrust in Othello's mind by claiming that he found Desdemona's handkerchief—Othello's first gift to her —in Cassius' room. It was only a matter of time before Othello was convinced that his wife had been unfaithful to him.

Noble-minded as he was, he might never have believed Iago's insinuations except that he had always harbored a doubt that a white woman would remain in love with him. He was proud of being a Moor, but knew that his kind were regarded with hatred and scorn. Preying on Othello's one weak spot—his love of Desdemona and his fear of losing her—Iago finally made him believe that he had been a novelty to his wife and she was now tired of him.

The Othello who went to Desdemona's bedroom and smothered her was a man driven temporarily mad with jealousy, self-doubt and wounded pride. Afterward when he knew the truth, he spoke to the other officers of Cyprus, before he fell upon his own sword:

> . . . I pray you, in your letters,
> When you shall these unlucky deeds relate,
> Speak of me as I am; nothing extenuate,
> Nor set down aught in malice: then must you speak
> Of one that loved not wisely but too well;
> Of one, not easily jealous, but, being wrought,
> Perplex'd in the extreme . . .

Then, as he died, believing he was speaking once more to his beloved wife, he murmured in heartbroken penitence: "I kiss'd thee ere I kill'd thee . . ."

On November 1 *Othello* was shown at Hampton Court. Queen Anne preferred the comedies but King James prided himself on his intellect and declared himself thrilled by *Othello*.

The former Admiral's Company had been taken under the protection of young Prince Henry and the Queen had her own players. Theatres and acting companies flourished under the new reign; writers and actors made more money than ever before— yet the quality of the plays deteriorated, except for those written by Shakespeare and Jonson.

The new writers, particularly Beaumont and Fletcher, catered to the whims of the court, which had none of the lusty, hearty zest for life that flourished during Elizabeth's reign. There was a sickly sentimentality and a touch of nastiness about them. Evil was brought in deliberately to shock people or make them snigger.

Shakespeare was filled with loathing and disgust for it all. He saw nothing about him but evidences of inhumanity, meanness, vileness. The court behaved in a scandalous fashion. The businessmen of London grew surly under the laws of King James. Quarreling among religious groups increased. And with this sickness of soul had come also the plague to once again turn London into a hell of dying men's screams, filled with the stench of bloated corpses.

Ever since the Essex rebellion and Southampton's abuse of his friendship, Shakespeare had been searching desperately for a way to understand people's behavior and yet continue to have compassion for them. Now he found himself overwhelmed by their misery.

In *King Lear* he found a measure of release as he poured all his demons of despair into the pages of the play.

It was the story of an aging king of Britain, Lear, who felt that the time had come for him to divide his kingdom among his three daughters. He decided that each of them would receive a piece in proportion to the amount of love that each one declared she had for him. Two of the daughters stated their love in extravagant terms, but the third one, Cordelia, could not bring herself to fawn and flatter her father. Lear, not comprehending the situation, was furious at her simple declaration of devotion.

Once in power, the two eldest daughters treated their father so badly that he went insane and wandered about with only his devoted fool to keep him company. Hoping to restore her father to the throne, Cordelia went to France to gather an army to depose her evil sisters, but the forces which Cordelia brought back were defeated in battle; she was imprisoned and finally hanged. Old Lear tried to defend her but was unable to do so. He died, brokenhearted, with her in his arms.

The Tragedy of King Lear was pitiless, relentless tragedy. The good Cordelia did not escape. The selfish Lear was punished. One evil sister was poisoned by the other, who afterward stabbed herself. There was no mercy, no justice, no last minute happy ending. Only the fact that each character was such a magnificent study of human nature saved the play and made it one of Shakespeare's finest works.

In the spring of 1604 the King's Players were invited to Oxford where they performed *King Lear, Hamlet* and other Shakespeare plays. Here the playwright was feted, praised and looked upon with awe by the students. But the adulation meant nothing to him, and suddenly he felt he must escape and seek peace. He told Burbage, and made his way to Stratford.

For the first weeks at home he was still sunk in melancholy. He could not work. He slept badly. He wanted no company but his own thoughts. Then, slowly, the magic spell of the countryside began to work its charm. The forest, the sweet, clean-smelling meadows, the spring rains, seemed to cleanse the whole world; the familiar, easy ways of the town comforted him. He took long walks, visiting remembered places. He lay for hours by the river Avon, watching its peaceful meanderings.

Above all else, he rediscovered his family. Until now he had only been an occasional visitor at New Place—Anne and his children were strangers to him. Now he found that he had two delightful daughters: Susanna, saucy and brimming with life at twenty-one, and quiet, loving Judith who was nearly twenty.

They loved him and so obviously enjoyed being with him that he marveled. What had he ever given them except what money could buy?

Treachery he found in the world, but what was that against the steadfast devotion of his wife? Misery there might be, but there was also the laughing buoyancy of Susanna; and Judith's gentle nature was proof that sweetness still existed in people.

To complete the cure, Ben Jonson arrived for a visit, giving Will the intellectual stimulation he needed. Jonson was riding the crest of popularity at court with the pageants and masques he designed and for which he wrote the speeches and songs. The two men spent countless hours talking and arguing in the drawing room of New Place or pacing back and forth in its beautiful garden.

"One more day of this and you will be chafing for London," Will told Ben. "However, Stratford suits me, and I would be content to remain here for the rest of my life. I intend to live here as much of the time as possible, but I am still part of the company. The Globe needs plays, so I am writing one that takes place in Scotland, which should please the King."

"What is the name of the play?" Jonson asked.

"*Macbeth.*"

"A comedy?"

Shakespeare shook his head. "No, I am not of that humor." He had been leading his friend toward a bench in the garden, but as they neared it he put his hand on Ben's arm and steered him away, not wishing to interrupt the young people seated there. "Hush! Don't let them see us. It is Susanna, being courted by a fine young man—Dr. John Hall."

Jonson, casting a backward look, liked what he saw of the suitor, for he appeared to be sturdy, dependable and intelligent. "I hope the young man is worthy of Susanna."

"I think he is," was the answer.

Jonson was delighted to see the new happiness and serenity in Shakespeare's face. That night they sat before the fire in the drawing room and played some of the games of Will's childhood which were his mother's favorites. She was elderly now but still quick in wit, and there was a great deal of laughter from the table where she and Ben Jonson matched cleverness. Shakespeare had often wondered why Jonson's brawling, swashbuckling nature did not repel him as had Greene's and Marlowe's and Kyd's. Watching him now, he realized that it was the tenderness underneath Jonson's roughness that appealed to him.

When Jonson left for London, Shakespeare began concentrated work on the play. His mental and spiritual health had so improved that in writing *Macbeth* he did not pour his own pain into it.

This was the tragic story of a Scottish general and his wife whose craving for power led them to murder their king. Once committed to their course, there was no turning back: Macbeth had to kill his fellow general because he was afraid Banquo suspected him of murdering the king. Lady Macbeth, who had determined to be hard and cold and unfeeling, became insane. Walking in her sleep, seeing the blood on her hands which she could not wash off, she cried:

> Out, damned spot! Out, I say . . .
> Fie, my lord, fie! . . .
> What need we fear who knows it,
> When none can call our power to account?
> Yet, who would have thought
> The old man to have had so much blood on him?

Macbeth was so driven by his guilt that he consulted the Queen of Evil about the future. Hers was a strange prophecy: MacDuff, a powerful lord, will fight against Macbeth but Macbeth will not be defeated until Birnam Wood moves against the castle. The prophecy came true and Macbeth was slain.

When the play was finished, Shakespeare went to London to attend to its production and settle other urgent matters.

"If we could rent a smaller, indoor theatre," Burbage and Heminge suggested, "we could play the year round in London.

The Globe is open to the skies. When it rains or storms we must stop our performances and hope to be invited to appear in the law courts or private mansions."

Shakespeare agreed, but reminded them, "There will be difficulties. Richard, you will have to learn to tone down the great thunder of your voice. I suspect that playing indoors will change our style of acting."

They rented the Blackfriars Theatre, and soon found that in one week they could make more money there than they could in three at the Globe, because they attracted wealthier audiences who could afford to pay higher prices.

While *Macbeth* continued to be the most popular play at the Globe, Shakespeare revived his light comedies for the Blackfriars and also began to write *Antony and Cleopatra*. Perhaps it was seeing his own daughter falling in love; perhaps it was the renewed cheerfulness in his own heart and the consolation that Stratford and his family had brought him. Whatever it was, this play was very different from the last few he had written.

True, *Antony and Cleopatra* ended in tragedy, but not a bitter one. The two lovers were greater in death than in their lives.

He was one of the three men ruling Rome; she, Queen of Egypt. They had first met in Egypt, and Cleopatra had kept him at her pleasure-loving, extravagant court when he should have been helping to put down unrest at home. At news of his wife's death, Antony tore himself away, went back to Rome and married Octavia, the sister of Octavius Caesar, to preserve the peace that had been threatened by his long absence.

But Antony could not stay away from Cleopatra and rejoined her in Alexandria. Octavius Caesar became furious and prepared for war against Antony and Cleopatra. Antony's admirers felt that his love for Cleopatra had destroyed his wisdom and military genius, and they deserted him. When the war went against him, Antony fell on his own sword and died in Cleopatra's arms. Caesar planned to take Cleopatra triumphantly back to Rome as his captive, but she had put a poisonous snake to her breast preferring in death to be with Antony. Their's was a love so great that nothing—not country, not duty, not death—could keep them apart.

Shakespeare said of Cleopatra: "Age cannot wither her; nor custom stale her infinite variety." Soon all of London was saying the same thing about his latest play. They could not get enough of *Antony and Cleopatra*, and it had to be performed over and over again.

Fame, riches, honors were bestowed upon William Shakespeare. Dressed in scarlet livery by the special orders of the King, he and the other players of his company were proclaimed Grooms of the Chamber, with no court duties except to be present on special occasions to impress foreign ambassadors. Shakespeare, the foremost playwright and poet of his day, would have been gladly received in any palace or mansion; he was idolized by the younger writers.

All London was at his feet, yet he spurned it. It was no longer the gay, quick city that he had loved. The prosperity begun under Elizabeth had continued to expand; English ships grew bolder, pushing on to new countries and greater wealth. But the people were divided and unhappy. James was unable to understand that the English people would not do his bidding merely because he demanded that they do so.

Shakespeare, displaying an incredible boldness that no one else would have dared to show, wrote *Coriolanus*, the story of a Roman general who, because he despised the common people, was banished from Rome and killed. London audiences understood it, but the King fancied himself too much the "good schoolmaster" of his people to see himself as Coriolanus.

"Is it any wonder that I prefer Stratford to this gloomy city?" Shakespeare asked of Jonson one day as they sat at their familiar table at THE MERMAID. Looking about him, he had a feeling this might be his last time in the tavern, with its ceiling beams darkened by the smoke of many cheerful, roaring fires. Memories of Marlowe, Raleigh, Kyd—and Southampton—crowded this room with their gay, boisterous ghosts. "*This* London suits you, Ben.

Here you can find all the material for your satires, but I do not find comedy in the actions of either commoners or the court."

Ben's eyes lighted with savage glee. "Let me tell you of a satire I contemplate writing—I shall call it *Bartholomew Fair*. If my audiences squirm to see themselves in my characters, so much the better. I'll give them no Falstaff to dote on, no fairyland for them to play in. I'll show people as they really are—humbugs, all of them. I call a spade a spade."

Three younger playwrights—Thomas Heywood, George Wilkins, John Fletcher—arrived at that moment to join them. Shakespeare listened to their cynical talk. He did not like it. Jonson had a robust health in his plays, but not these men. These new writers did not care or suffer for human beings: they laughed at humanity. Scandal, fashion, gossip—these went into their plays.

He got up and bade the men good-by. "My brother Edmund is ill and I must see him before I leave for Stratford."

"Stratford again?" Heywood asked. "We see you much too seldom, Will."

Smiling, he told them, "My daughter Susanna is to be married soon and I want to be there for the wedding."

The plague had again struck London and Edmund died of it. Shakespeare sadly attended to his burial in the church of St. Saviour's, only a little way from the Globe Theatre, regretting that they had not become closer during their time together in the city. His brother had begun his acting career just as Shakespeare began to spend less and less time at the theatre.

After his sad task, Will turned gratefully toward home and his family. Even his mother's grief for Edmund was eased by her joy at Susanna's marriage to John Hall. The event drew Will and Anne closer together than they had ever been. The Halls lived a short distance from them, and the birth of their first grandchild, Elizabeth, in February of 1608 brought Will and Anne great happiness. The baby girl wrapped herself around Will's heart. He had missed so much of the childhood of his own children, he could hardly be parted from Elizabeth.

When his mother died shortly after the wedding in 1607, Will grieved deeply but he knew that she had lived a rich, full life and that her latter years had been proud, comfortable, happy ones.

There was much for him to do in Stratford, managing his various properties, and he reluctantly started on a new play, *Cymbeline*.

A messenger from Burbage came to see him. "The Globe and Blackfriars desperately need new plays," read Burbage's note. "Would you write one for us, quickly?"

There was a story Shakespeare knew very well. He had read it in Plutarch's *Life of Marcus Antonius*, then again in Painter's *Palace of Pleasure*. It was the story of the rich *Timon of Athens*, who generously loaned or gave all his money away, only to find that when he was poor none of his former friends would help him. The angry Timon cursed all mankind, went to live as a hermit in a cave near the sea, where he uncovered a treasure of gold. He remained a hermit and shared the gold only with an old faithful servant and with the general Alcibiades. Then Timon learned that Alcibiades was going to march on Athens and take vengeance on all his former friends.

It was an easy play for Shakespeare to write, enjoying the writing, knowing that it was certain to be successful, with its neat story of justice triumphant and ingratitude punished.

When Shakespeare left for London that Christmas of 1608 to be present at court for King James' Revels, he paid a visit to his friend Richard Field. The printer and his wife had grown older and portly, but they were unchanged in their warm welcome.

While Mistress Field bustled about in her usual way, arranging a supper for them, Will told about Susanna's marriage and her baby daughter, about Judith being courted by young Thomas Quiney, and spoke of his great contentment with Stratford and his home life. Then their talk turned to their work. "By the way, Ben Jonson has collected his plays and they are to be published in one volume called his *Works*," Richard said. "I would like to publish yours."

"There are changes I would like to make in some of them—

a line here and there that does not satisfy me. I will do it, Richard. I am not acting any more and have the time."

Before Will left, Richard showed him a novel that George Wilkins had written, *The Painful Adventures of Pericles*. Shakespeare became so interested in the story that the next day he got in touch with Wilkins, learned that he had already begun a play about Pericles and offered to collaborate with him.

Wilkins was delighted, even though when the play was sent back to him finished, very little of his own writing remained.

The story of *Pericles, Prince of Tyre*, is the story of a family separated then reunited. This theme had a special meaning for Shakespeare. Just so, he was now truly finding his own. He still kept his rooms in London because he needed a place he could come to and work when necessary, and his landlord, Christopher Mountjoy, had become something of a friend.

But he preferred his well-furnished, comfortable study in New Place, with Anne and baby Elizabeth nearby. Here he finished *Cymbeline*, but it had little of the power and force of his earlier writings. There were lines in it that reflected his weariness with ambition and his longing to get rid of the demands of his profession.

The play that followed was called *The Winter's Tale*, taken from a romance entitled *Pandosta*. Shakespeare had created many wonderful women—from Juliet in *Romeo and Juliet* to Portia in *Julius Caesar*. Now, Hermione in *The Winter's Tale* was his answer to the cheap, vulgar women who were entertaining the crowds in the plays of Beaumont and Fletcher. Hermione personified womanhood in the fullest, deepest sense, for she remained a loyal, steadfast, loving wife despite all the hurt and sorrow she was forced to bear. When he created Hermione, Shakespeare might have been thinking of his own wife Anne, who had remained steadfast through all his absences and whose virtues he was honoring for all time.

17

The writing of these two plays and the work of handling his properties in Stratford, kept Will fully occupied during the years 1609 and 1610. The spring of 1611 found him in semi-retirement from the stage, and spending almost all of his time in Stratford.

That spring was a particularly beautiful one. He rose early to watch the morning mist shroud the garden, the trees, the shrubs with swirls of soft, pearly gray fog. Then, as the sun broke through, the miracle and glory of dawn kept him as breathless as he had been as a boy. Before the rest of the house was stirring, he would be out, walking through the fields and meadows, in the forest or along the river. Something was reborn in him that spring: his poetic awareness of the beauty and mystery of nature came flooding back to fill him with greater rapture than before.

He had learned, bitterly, that there was ugliness and evil in the world. Now, watching a shy deer drinking at a forest pool, gazing at carpets of violets half-hidden behind a mossy log, listening to the sweet calls of birds, he wondered if the ugliness that came from man could not be tamed by man. In his mind he gave this evil shape a name—Caliban. He would put Caliban into a play.

Will began to come home from his morning walks with his head full of poetic fancies, and slowly the plot of *The Tempest* formed, and when he was finally ready to write, his genius was burning with a flame brighter than ever.

Never before had he created such fabulous characters as Prospero, a former duke of Milan, his daughter Miranda, the fairy sprite Ariel, the romantic young Prince Ferdinand—and that wicked, misshapen monster, Caliban. The play was filled with sheer enchantment and wonderful imagery, haunting poetry and immortal charm; yet it did not lack the human emotions—love and hate—that gave his characters flesh-and-blood reality.

The banished duke and his daughter dwelt on a lonely island, where Prospero practiced magic, commanding the sprite to do his bidding until released. Caliban, the symbol of evil in the world, also served the magician, but was always waiting his chance to harm his master. When Ferdinand arrived on the island, he fell in love with Miranda, but was unhappy because he feared that his father had drowned. The provocative Ariel taunted the prince with his song:

> Full fathom five thy father lies;
> Of his bones are coral made;
> Those are pearls that were his eyes:
> Nothing of him that doth fade,
> But doth suffer a sea-change
> Into something rich and strange. . . .

Prospero, working his magic, finally united father and son, gave his daughter in marriage to Ferdinand and bade farewell to the enchanted island.

Shakespeare, in *The Tempest*, was also taking leave of his magic world of imagination and poetry. And, just as Prospero set his dainty Ariel free, with the words "I shall miss thee . . . ," so Shakespeare wistfully said good-by to the spirit-genius of poetic creation at his command, which had for so long done his bidding. Through Prospero, Shakespeare expressed his own desire:

> I here abjure . . .
> I'll break my staff,
> Bury it certain fathoms in the earth . . .
> I'll drown my book.

But Shakespeare was still bound to his work. He had a responsibility to his theatres, and the King could still demand both his presence and his work. In 1612 his brother Gilbert died. This grief made him more reluctant to leave Stratford, but for the Christmas Revels that same year Will was ordered to appear at court. King James' daughter, Elizabeth, was being married to Frederick V, Elector-Palatine of the Rhine. Such an event called for the most extravagant entertainment that the court could provide and, naturally, England's greatest playwright had to be present and have a new work to be performed.

Will wrote another new play, *The Famous History of the Life of King Henry VIII*. After it was performed before the King and Queen and the betrothed Prince and Princess, Shakespeare had to remain in London for the festivities that went on, month after month, into the spring and summer of 1613.

On July 29 *King Henry VIII* was to be presented at the Globe. Will walked into the huge round theatre that afternoon noting how badly worn were the wooden steps leading up to the balconies, how chipped and scratched was the paint. He could not help but feel sad to see these scars, for they were proof of the many thousands of spectators who had come to this theatre to laugh or cry or shout or be stunned into silence.

He went backstage to find Richard Burbage in the dressing room, penciling wrinkles on his face to make himself look older for the role of Wolsey, Cardinal of York and Lord Chancellor of England. Richard rose and pulled the heavy cardinal's mantle around his shoulders. "Do I look the part, Will?" he asked.

Shakespeare smiled, remembering the young, handsome, earnest Richard. He was still good-looking—but neither of them was young any more. Will was forty-nine and Burbage nearly the same age.

"I wish I were acting with you today, Richard," he said thoughtfully. "Sometimes I long for the stage and the days that are past. Do you remember how we tore down the old Theatre and carted the wood here to build the Globe? Do you remember when I wanted to write plays as fine as Marlowe's and you wanted to be rival to Alleyn?"

Burbage smiled at him with affection. "And how we dreamed

as young men of having our own theatre someday?" He looked at Shakespeare as Will had looked at him, thinking how little his friend had changed. Older, yes, but still slim and still possessing that same gentle manner. Will's hair had receded slightly so that his forehead seemed higher and nobler; there were lines of sorrow and laughter around his eyes, the chestnut hair had a few streaks of silver—but the expression on his face was more youthful than it had been for many years.

As the other actors came in to make ready for the performance, Shakespeare drew aside the curtain and looked at the noisy, eager crowd. William Sly, who was playing the Archbishop of Canterbury, joined him.

"Are you certain," he asked, "that you still wish me to deliver the tribute to Queen Elizabeth?" The play was the story of Elizabeth's father, Henry VIII, and it ended with the birth of the baby girl and the prophecy of her greatness. "King James was provoked by those lines when we played before him. He does not like to be reminded of how much England loved Elizabeth."

Shakespeare held the curtain further aside for Sly to see the audience. "We play to them," he said firmly, "not to James. They are the men and women of England who loved our good Queen. Deliver the tribute, Sly, and when you come to the passage—'Good grows with her: In her days every man shall eat in safety'—speak those lines with all thy heart's feeling for England."

Shakespeare found a place where he could watch the stage, but his attention wandered instead to the intent faces of the audience. How often had he called them names, as does any actor who fears that the people will laugh in the wrong places or boo him off the stage. Yet he knew he loved them. They were men and women like himself and they came to see plays for the same reason he had written and acted in them. Emotions had to be shared, else a man wandered alone and afraid all his life. He had shared his thoughts, his loves, his fears, his dreams, with them and they had brought their own emotions to the theatre to respond to his.

The second act was to open with a blare of horns. But in addition to the cornets, which Will expected to hear, came the louder blast of guns being discharged. "The fools!" he said to himself. "I did not ask for the firing of the guns to announce the King's entrance. I wonder who was responsible for this?" But his anger ebbed away as his thoughts turned back to the stage and the audience.

Suddenly there was a loud scream from the crowd, then the sound of people in the balconies jumping to their feet, an indistinguishable yell, and then the cry was picked up and echoed all over the Globe:

"Fire!"

The players stopped. Shakespeare ran onto the stage and looked up to where horrified spectators were pointing—to the thatched roof of the shadow over the stage. The thatch had been set afire by the guns and was blazing in leaping tongues of red and yellow.

"Fire!"

Within seconds the whole theatre was in pandemonium. In the chaos people rushed this way and that, shoving and pushing those in front of them to reach the doors; men in the first balcony leaped to the ground, landing on the shoulders and backs of those below them. The upper balcony steps were choked as frantic crowds struggled to get down the narrow aisles. On stage old Heminge raised his powerful voice to calm the fleeing audience, but it was no use.

The flames leaped from thatch to the wooden sides of the circular building and sparks that dropped onto the rushes below were stamped out. Here and there clothing caught fire, causing the person to scream until someone beat it out. Smoke was filling the air so rapidly that everyone was gasping for breath.

It was a miracle that, with only a few exits to the building, the large crowd got out safely and there was no serious injury. The players themselves departed just before the whole Globe went up in a great tower of flames.

Panting and gasping, Shakespeare and Burbage stood outside

and watched their great dream burn itself to the ground. Their own hands had sawed and carried the very timbers that were now blazing. It was more than wood and straw that was being destroyed—it was thousands of memories and triumphs and heartaches.

Suddenly Will saw on the ground beside him a pile of manuscripts. Wonderingly, he turned them over. They were the manuscripts of his plays. He looked at the company with tears in his eyes; none had tried to save his own personal belongings, but each had carried out one or more of these plays, the company's most priceless possessions.

"We will build again, Will," Burbage said.

"Of course," Will answered, but in his heart he knew that the Globe was finished for him. The King's Men would rebuild a theatre, but he would have no part in it. And, though the sight of the burning building was painful, he was almost glad. The last link of the bonds had snapped. He was free.

This time his retirement to Stratford was complete. He wrote no more new plays, but took his old ones and polished them, making a few revisions so that they could be printed as a complete set of *Works*.

He remained happily, peacefully, among his family and friends. The home of Susanna and her husband was so close to New Place that they were almost a part of the household that Anne now ruled with dignity and pride. The youngest daughter, Judith, married Thomas Quiney early in the year 1616 and the wedding symbolized for William Shakespeare a rounding-out of his life.

He had not long to live.

On March 25 of that same year he made his will. On April 20 Ben Jonson and Michael Drayton came to New Place to visit their old friend. Shakespeare found it wonderful to see them again, even though he was feeling very tired. He spent a long and late evening with them talking about the new theatre and the old. Jonson belonged to the new school of writing, but Drayton had known Marlowe and Kyd and Greene. He and Shakespeare reminisced for hours over those early days, while Jonson teased them both for being sentimental.

After they left, Will walked up and down in the garden, feeling restless. The talk with Drayton had brought back half-forgotten memories, which now came crowding back as he paced. The ghosts of Kempe and Tarleton walked with him, telling him how to play his very first scene on a stage. He relived that glorious moment when, watching *Tamburlaine*, he made up his mind to become a writer of plays.

The night was chill, the hour was late, but still he walked and remembered. In the garden with him was Richard the Crookback—oh, how well Burbage had played him! He saw a light in the second story of his house—was that not Juliet on the balcony? He was surrounded by all of them—the tragic, somber Hamlet, the saucy Rosalind, the noble Portia, the mad wandering Lear, Cleopatra in her glorious raiments of Egypt, the sly Iago whispering to the proud Othello—and of course that huge, lovable scoundrel Falstaff, holding his sides while his tub of a belly shook with laughter.

Then other ghosts joined him: the dashing, impatient Earl of Essex, young, handsome Southampton, for whom he now felt only forgiveness and affection. His Dark Lady smiled at him and he took a step toward her . . .

But it was cold in the garden. He shivered, remembering where he was. Tired now, he waved his hand and smiled and all the ghosts vanished. He went into the house to Anne.

He had been overtired. The evening chill had crept into his body. That night, fever struck him swiftly; he was ill and worsened with every hour. His son-in-law, Dr. Hall, was sent for but nothing could be done to save him.

On April 23, in the beginning of his fifty-third year, Will Shakespeare died. The greatest playwright the world had ever known was gone and all England mourned his loss. On April 25 he was buried in Trinity Church in Stratford-on-Avon.

But the creator of those glorious plays and poems lives on and will live forever. In *Julius Caesar* occur the prophetic lines:

> . . . How many ages hence
> Shall this our lofty scene be acted o'er
> In states unborn and accents yet unknown.

Throughout the centuries since his death, William Shakespeare's works have been performed before audiences in almost every country of the world, in almost every language.

Untold millions have read and loved his memorable plays; his sonnets are the pride of the English tongue. Will Shakespeare's times have changed, but his characters are ageless.

AUTHOR'S NOTE

Thousands of brilliant, scholarly books have been written on William Shakespeare's life, his plays, poems, philosophy, stagecraft, his sense of wit and of tragedy. To venture to write a *dramatized* biography of the world's greatest dramatist was reckless, indeed. Yet, when my publishers suggested it, I welcomed the challenge because I remembered my own high school days, how little I was told of the man, himself, and how curious I was about him.

Who was William Shakespeare?

Many facts of his life are known. For the rest, I found it was possible to logically bridge the gaps unknown. If my speculations and theories displease some authorities on Shakespeare, I hope that at least they find in them a humble attempt to be faithful to the character of Shakespeare as revealed in his plays and poetry, and deduced from the known facts.

It was dialogue and conversation which troubled me the most. How could I put words into the mouth of William Shakespeare, who had written the most beautiful words in the English language? Therefore, when Shakespeare talks to his friends or fellow-actors in this book, I have used lines, words, excerpts from his own writings—wherever possible. This is not a device or a trick. I doubt that Shakespeare had two entirely different vocabularies: one for his everyday speech and one for his writings.

Several mistakes have been made deliberately. Shakespeare wrote the second part of *Henry VI* before he wrote the first part, but it would have been confusing if the story of English history were not told in sequence. *Julius Caesar* was probably not the first production given at the newly-built Globe Theatre but it could have been performed very shortly after.

I found such enormous research material both in the British Museum in London, and in the Folger Library in Washington, D. C., that I am able to list only a small number of the books which were helpful. Special mention must be made of John Dover Wilson's *The Essential Shakespeare*, Cambridge University Press, London, New York, 1960. Also, of *Shakespeare's England*, two vols., Oxford University Press, London, 1917; F. E. Halliday's *Shakespeare in his Age*, Gerald Duckworth & Co., Ltd., London, 1956; A *Survey of London* by John Stowe in 1598, ed. by C. L. Kingsford, two vols., Oxford University Press, 1908; *Henslowe's Diary* and *Henslowe's Papers*, edited by W. W. Greg, pub. by Bullen, London, 1904; *Shakespeare Without Tears*, by Margaret Webster, the World Publishing Company, New York, 1957; A *Companion to Shakespeare Studies*, edited by H. Granville-Barker and G. B. Harrison, Doubleday and Company, 1960; Alfred Harbage's *Shakespeare's Audience*, Columbia University Press, New York, 1941; J. C. Adams' *The Globe Playhouse: Its Design and Equipment*, Harvard University Press, 1942; Ivor Brown's *Shakespeare*, Collins, London, 1949; *The Complete Works of William Shakespeare*, ed. by W. A. Wright, Doubleday and Co., New York, 1936; A *Complete Concordance of Shakespeare*, John Bartlett, A.M., Macmillan and Co., Ltd., London and New York, 1956.

INDEX

184

185

New Place, 134, 157, 166, 173, 179
Newgate Prison, 99
Newington, 127
North, Sir Thomas, 38

Octavia, 169
Old Bailey, 139
Oliver, 143
Ophelia, 158-59
Orlando, 143
Orlando, 101
Othello, 161, 163-65
Oxford, 21, 27, 44-46, 166
Oxford, Earl of, 65, 67

Painful Adventures of Pericles, The, 173
Painter, William, 31, 172
Pandosta, 173
Papists, 18
Parker, Matthew, 24
Pembroke's Men, Earl of, 74, 78, 80, 81
Pericles, 173
Petruchio, 102-03
Philip, King of Spain, 26-27, 52, 130
Phillips, Augustine, 101, 130, 156
plague, the, 101, 103, 118-20, 122-23, 136, 142
plays, by William Shakespeare
  All's Well That Ends Well, 159
  Antony and Cleopatra, 169-70
  As You Like It, 142-43
  Comedy of Errors, The, 86, 100
  Coriolanus, 170
  Cymbeline, 172-73
  Hamlet, 158-59, 161
  Henry IV, Part I, 135; *Part II*, 136
  Henry V, 138
  Henry VI, Part I, 75-79; *Part II*, 80; *Part III*, 88-90
  Henry VIII, 176-77
  Julius Caesar, 144-50
  King John, 134

King Lear, 165-66
Love's Labour Lost, 117-18, 120
Macbeth, 167-68
Measure for Measure, 160
Merchant of Venice, The, 130-32
Merry Wives of Windsor, 142
Midsummer Night's Dream, A, 122-23, 129
Much Ado About Nothing, 138
Othello, 161, 163-65
Pericles, Prince of Tyre, 173
Richard II, 128, 152, 155-56
Richard III, 92-95
Romeo and Juliet, 119, 122, 123-24, 129
Taming of the Shrew, 101-03
Tempest, The, 174-75
Timon of Athens, 172
Titus Andronicus, 87
Troilus and Cressida, 159
Twelfth Night, 150-51
Two Gentlemen of Verona, The, 105
Winter's Tale, The, 173
Plutarch, 172
Plautus, 86
Pleasure, The Palace of, 31, 172
poetry, by William Shakespeare
  Lucrece, 122
  sonnets, to Southampton, 126; about the Dark Lady, 129
  Venus and Adonis, 105, 107, 111, 121
Poley, Robert, 121
Polonius, 158-59, 161
Pope, Thomas, 56, 62, 63-67, 101, 137, 146
Portia, 131
Prospero, 174-75
Protestants, 24
Puritans, 20, 162

Queen's Men, the, 39-40, 60, 69, 70, 74, 81, 87-88, 93, 101
Quiney, Adrian, 9
Quiney, Thomas, 172, 179

187

Shakespeare, William—*continued*
war with Spain, 127; forms new
company, 127; writes about divine right of kings in *Richard
II*, 128; enjoys business affairs,
128-30; his *Merchant of Venice*,
130-32; death of son, 133; buys
mansion in Stratford, 134; writes
Henry IV, 135-36; is partner in
Globe Theatre, 138; friendship
with Jonson, 140-41; two more
successful plays, 142-43; his
Julius Caesar at the Globe, 144-
50; is distressed by Southampton's behavior, 151; is suspected
of complicity in rebellion, 155-
56; death of father, 157; other
family matters, 157; his inner
torture revealed in *Hamlet*, 158-
59; presents *Othello* for King,
163-65; pours his despair into
King Lear, 165-66; returns to
Stratford for peace, 166; his
health and spirit improve, 168;
writes *Macbeth*, 168; his *Antony
and Cleopatra* very popular, 169-
70; is foremost playwright and
poet, 170; attends to family affairs, 171; collaborates with
Wilkins, 173; in semi-retirement, 174; his genius brighter
than ever in *The Tempest*, 174-
75; writes *Henry VIII* to honor
princess' betrothal, 176; burning
of Globe, 178; retires completely
to Stratford, 179; death of, 180
Sheffield Castle, 24
Shepherd's Bush, 47
Shoreditch, 138
Shotover, Forest of, 44
Shottery, 29, 32
Shylock, 130-32
Sly, William, 101, 177
Somerset, Duke of, 72, 76
Southampton, Earl of, 67, 84-85,
86, 96-98, 100, 105, 106-09,
111-113, 114-16, 118, 122, 124-

27, 132, 139, 141, 150-52, 154-
56
Southward, 138
Spain, 26-27, 52-53, 70-71, 127,
130, 132, 134
Spenser, Edmund, 38
Strand, the, 142
Strange, Lord, 68, 123
Strange, Lord, company of. *See*
Lord Strange's Men
Stratford-on-Avon, 9-10, 25, 36, 39,
104, 119, 122, 133-34, 135, 157,
166, 174, 179, 180
Stuart, Mary, 24, 52-53
Suffolk, Earl of, 77
Swan Theatre, 138

Talbot, General, 78-79
Tamburlaine, 64, 68, 81, 96
Taming of the Shrew, The, 101-03,
127
Tarleton, Richard, 40-42, 44, 47,
60, 65-67, 69, 70
Tempest, The, 174-75
Temple Garden, 72, 76
Thames River, 53, 61, 71, 101, 141
Three Ladies of London, 56
Timon of Athens, 172
Titchfield, 113, 114ff.
Titus Andronicus, 87, 127
Trinity Church, 180
Troilus and Cressida, 159
Tudor, Henry, 94
Twelfth Night, 150-51
Tyburn, 130

Udall, Nicholas, 22
Uxbridge Road, 47

Vautrollier, Master, 27, 38, 52, 57-
58
Venice, 131, 163
Venus, 105
Venus and Adonis, 105, 107, 111,
121
Verges, 138

189

About the Author

IRIS NOBLE grew up on a ranch in the Crow's Nest Pass between Canada's Alberta and British Columbia. Her parents were American and when she was eleven they moved to Oregon. After graduating from the University of Oregon, she moved to Los Angeles and got her first job as a secretary at station KFI-KECA. She left there to work for Fawcett Publications and later was publicity director for a theatre-restaurant. After her marriage she came to New York City where she did freelance writing. In recent years she has made her home in San Francisco and has been devoting herself to writing both in the field of biography and teen-age fiction.